ACID

COOKBOOK

Defeat Your Disease With the Best Acid Reflux Recipes

(Easy Anti Acid Diet Meal Plans & Recipes to Heal Gerd)

Daniel Hughes

Published by Alex Howard

© **Daniel Hughes**

All Rights Reserved

*Acid Reflux Cookbook: Defeat Your Disease With the Best Acid Reflux Recipes
(Easy Anti Acid Diet Meal Plans & Recipes to Heal Gerd)*

ISBN 978-1-77485-003-9

Legal & Disclaimer

The information contained in this book is not designed to replace or take the place of any form of medicine or professional medical advice. The information in this book has been provided for educational and entertainment purposes only.

Table of contents

Part 1

INTRODUCTION

The gastroesophageal reflux disease (GERD) occurs when the lower esophageal sphincter (LES) valve controlling the passage of the contents of the esophagus into the stomach, this alters or relaxes inappropriately, allowing the materials turn into the esophagus, thus irritating, the mucosa caused symptomatology and characteristic complications.

Gastroesophageal reflux is different from hiatal hernia, but both diseases make feedingverydifficult, producing very annoying symptoms. In the following content, I will explain what it is and how is it's treated nutritionally.

CHAPTER 1: GENERAL DESCRIPTION

Gastroesophageal reflux disease occurs when stomach acid usually returns to the duct that connects the mouth to the stomach (esophagus). This flows in the opposite direction (acid reflux) and can irritate the lining of the esophagus.

Many people suffer from acid reflux often. Gastroesophageal reflux disease can be mild acid reflux, which occurs at least twice a week, or a moderate to severe acid reflux, which occurs at least once a week.

Most people can control the discomfort of gastroesophageal reflux disease with lifestyle changes or over-the-counter medications. However, some people with gastroesophageal reflux disease may need stronger medications or surgery to relieve symptoms.

Symptom

Some frequent signs and symptoms of gastroesophageal reflux disease are as follows:

A burning sensation in the chest (heartburn), usually after eating that may get worse at night

Chest pain
Difficulty to swallow

Regurgitation of food or sour liquids

The feeling of lumping in the throat

If you have acid reflux at night, you may also have the following:

Chronic cough
Laryngitis
New or worsening asthma

Sleep disturbance

When to consult the doctor

Seek immediate medical attention if you feel chest pain, especially if you also have shortness of breath or pain in your jaw or arm. They may be signs and symptoms of a heart attack.

Request a consultation with the doctor in the following cases:

If you have symptoms of severe or frequent gastroesophageal reflux disease.

If you take over-the-counter medications for heartburn more than twice a week.

How do you diagnose Gastroesophageal Reflux Disease?

When a patient experiences common symptoms of gastroesophageal reflux disease, mainly acidity and acid regurgitation, it is usually not necessary to perform additional tests before starting the treatment. If the symptoms do not respond to treatment, or if other symptoms such as weight loss, difficulty swallowing, or internal bleeding appear, additional studies may be necessary. Upper endoscopy is a test that uses a small tube with a light at its end to examine the esophagus, stomach, and duodenum (the first portion of the small intestine). Before performing this study, you will receive the necessary medications that will help you relax and reduce the discomfort you may feel. An upper endoscopy allows your doctor to observe the lining of the esophagus and detect any evidence of damage. A tissue biopsy can be performed using an instrument similar to a clamp. Obtaining a biopsy sample does not cause pain or discomfort.

Another test, known as pH control, measures the acid in the esophagus and can be performed either by inserting a small sensor at the time of completing the endoscopy or by placing a thin, flexible probe in the esophagus for 24 hours while Measure the acid content. This information is transmitted to a small recorder that is attached to the patient's belt. X-rays do not play any role in the initial evaluation of people with symptoms of reflux disease.

Causes

What are the causes of reflux?

The gastroesophageal reflux disease occurs when there is a disturbance between the defense mechanisms of the esophagus and stomach offensive mechanisms, such as acid and other juice and digestive enzymes. The passage of food from the esophagus to the stomach is controlled by the lower esophageal valve or sphincter (IAS). People living with this disease have an alteration in this valve. This is kept open for some time, thus, allowing the passage of content from one area to another.

Some dietary aspects or lifestyles can contribute to or increase the risk of suffering from gastroesophageal reflux, such as:

A high intake of alcohol, smoking, high consumption of irritating foods such as chocolate, pepper or spices, mint, coffee, foods high in fat. All this favors the relaxation of the lower esophageal sphincter, allowing the passage of stomach contents into the esophagus.

Many patients also have a hiatus hernia. Hiatus hernia consists of moving part of the stomach to the chest through the diaphragm, favoring gastroesophageal reflux. This is not the only cause since not everyone suffering from hiatus hernia also suffers from reflux.

On the other hand, other situations that produce an increase in intra-abdominal pressure may favor such reflux, overweight, or obesity, pregnancy, .etc.

Risk factor's

Some of the diseases that may increase the risk of gastroesophageal reflux disease are as follow:

Obesity
Lump in the upper stomach that goes up to the diaphragm (hiatus hernia)

Pregnancy
Connective tissue disorders, such as scleroderma

Delayed stomach emptying

Factors that can aggravate acid reflux include the following:

Smoke
Abundant meals or eating late at night

Eat certain foods (triggers), such as fried or fatty foods

Certain drinks, such as alcohol or coffee

Take certain medications, such as aspirin

Complications

Over time, chronic inflammation of the esophagus can cause the following:

1 Narrowing of the esophagus (esophageal stricture). Lesions in the lower part of the esophagus caused by stomach acid cause scar tissue to form. The scar tissue

narrows the path that food travels, causing difficulty in swallowing.

2 An open sore in the esophagus (esophageal ulcer). Stomach acid can wear down the esophageal tissue and cause the formation of an open wound. An esophageal ulcer can bleed, cause pain, and make swallowing difficult.

3 Pre-cancerous changes in the esophagus (Barrett's esophagus). The damage caused by the acid can cause alterations in the tissue that covers the lower part of the esophagus. These changes are associated with an increased risk of suffering from esophageal cancer.

CHAPTER 2: DIAGNOSIS AND EXPLORATION

In order avoid numerous and expensive examinations, there is first the interrogation stage when it is a young subject (under 50), that the present symptomatology is typical, and that there is no warning sign (such as dysphagia, anemia, weight loss).

Nevertheless, additional examinations are sometimes necessary for certain situations:

GERD symptoms after 50 years;

Symptoms of GERD treated who relapse;

GERD symptoms resistant to treatment;

GERD symptoms associated with atypical extra-digestive signs;

These exams are:

Eso-gastroduodenal endoscopy (EOGD) with or without a biopsy.

It is normal in 20 to 30% of cases. It allows searching for one of the main complications of GERD, which is the peptic esophagitis (related to the acid). It is an inflammation of the esophagus with erosions and ulcerations of the inner lining of the esophagus due to acid reflux. It is of variable severity and may be the cause of an endo-tracheoesophageal (EBO).

Endoscopy can also detect an associated abnormality such as hiatal hernia.

- esophageal pH-metry:

It measures the presence of acid in the esophagus and records reflux episodes and eventual agreement with symptoms experienced by the patient.

An intra-oesophageal sensor is used to analyze changes in the esophageal pH for 24 hours. The pH-metry is set up at typical symptomatology compatible with a possible GERD, causing respiratory disorders, pseudogene manifestations, and ENT problems.

It is also used in atypical symptomology of reflux, but without lesion of oesophagitis in subjects not improved by medical treatment well-conducted or relapsing immediately after stopping the medical treatment, then discuss a surgical indication.

Finally, it can be used in the context of pre-operative assessment or post-operative if complication or ineffectiveness occurs.

GERD becomes pathological when the time below pH 4 is more significant than 4.2% of the total recording time for 24 hours.

This examination is exciting to report atypical clinical signs to GERD, or in case of resistance to usual medical treatment. Sometimes, there is interest to couple this examination to oesophageal impedance meter, which allows measuring the volume of the reflux.

Other examinations are rarely performed but may be necessary, such as oesophageal transit baryta to see specific abnormalities (hiatal hernia, esophageal stenosis).

There is also oesophageal manometry for asserting a real hypotony of the SIO and evaluate the cause and not measure the consequences. The study of oesophageal peristalsis also makes it possible to search for associated motor disorders related to primary peristalsis with absence or reduction of peristaltic waves. It is useful in the pre-operative phase.

The link between GERD and Helicobacter pylori

Helicobacter pylori (HP) infection is one of the most common and most critical medical infections in the world. Infection with this gram-negative microaerobic bacterium is a factor in the development of peptic ulcer disease.

The nature of his relationship with GERD is still unclear. There is an ongoing debate about whether HP causes an increase in the prevalence or severity of GERD, or whether, on the contrary, people infected with this bacterium have fewer symptoms of GERD.

There are several studies in different countries that tend to develop various theories about the presence of HP and the prevalence of GERD.

A recent study comparing symptoms before and after HP eradication treatment in 95 patients showed that symptoms remained unchanged in the presence or absence of HP. In another study, neither the diagnosis nor the severity of oesophagitis in HP-infected patients was influenced by HP eradication. In these studies, the presence of HP would play no particular role in GERD.

Another study conducted in 2012 seeks to highlight the stage of oesophagitis due to GERD with the amount of HP present. Significant findings suggest the potential role of HP infection in the development of GERD.

A study published in January 2017 and conducted in Turkey showed that the rate of HP infection is high in place, but that the prevalence of GERD is very low. The presence of HP is here presented as reducing the incidence of GERD. Also, a different pattern of symptoms was observed where regurgitation was more common than heartburn.

Other studies tend to confirm this protective effect of HP infection on GERD.

A recent publication uses high-resolution manometry to measure pressure in the upper oesophageal sphincter down to the lower esophageal sphincter to see oesophageal motor function. This study combined this manometric measurement with a 24-hour pH monitoring analysis. The results of this study showed that patients with GERD and HP infected had improved esophageal peristalsis, increased the pressure of the LES, and reduced exposure to acid.

This would be because HP infection can cause atrophy of the gastric mucosa and alter acid production. Another hypothesis is that HP infection can stimulate the vagus nerve receptor on the bottom and the cardia of the stomach and increase gastrin secretion, which can increase the pressure of the SIO and reduce gastric reflux. These assumptions lead to a protective effect of HP's presence.

The majority of GERD prevalence studies were conducted using different methodologies and questionnaires, making it difficult to compare results. The link between HP and GERD is still very vague so far.

CHAPTER 3: DRUG AND SURGICAL TREATMENTS

The main objectives of these treatments are:

Relieve the patient.

Avoid complications.

There is progress over the past two decades in understanding and treating GOR, in part through the development and broader application of endoscopic monitoring and pH. Pharmacotherapy is considered the first-line treatment in GERD patients.

In many cases, the cause of reflux is untreated (e.g., a hiatal hernia), and recurrence occurs as soon as treatment is discontinued. Treatment can, therefore, be offered for very long periods.

1. Immediate but short-acting drugs

If the symptoms are typical and spaced (less than once a week), pastoral and hygienic-dietary periods are sufficient, combined if necessary, with the treatment of immediate effect and short duration of action such as alginates or antacids.

Antacids

These drugs decrease the acidity of gastric secretion by their buffering power and by directly neutralizing the hydrochloric acid present in the stomach. They do not act directly on THE GOR but protect the wall of the esophagus against pyrosis. Their duration of action is relatively short, but they can relieve the symptoms of acidity or heartburn on demand. They are administered after the meal and are mostly drinkable in the form of a drinkable suspension.

Several specialties exist:

Aluminum hydroxide - magnesium hydroxide: MAALOX®, XOLAAM®, GELOX®, which are drinkable suspensions. There is also a compressed form for MAALOX®.

Aluminum phosphate: PHOSPHALUGEL® (drinkable suspension in a bottle or dose bag), ROCGEL® (drinkable bottle suspension).

Calcium carbonate, heavy magnesium carbonate: RENNIE®.

At the counter, it is essential to point out that taking these specialties should be at a minimum interval of 2 hours with any other medication because by covering the gastric surface, they decrease their absorptions.

Alginates

Alginates form a viscous gel on the surface of the gastric contents, thus significantly decreasing the pyrosis symptom encountered in THE GOR.

Alginate - sodium bicarbonate (Na): GAVISCON drinkable suspension®
dimeticone - polysilane gel.

The significant side effect is high-dose constipation because the alginates are not resorbed; therefore, there is a risk of obstruction if consumed heavily.

For them to be fully active, they should be prescribed after the meal (if possible, 1 to 2 hours after). Similarly, like antacids, it is advisable not to take another specialty concurrently because of the risk of reducing its absorption.

2. Delayed but intense drugs

If relapses are early and frequent, continuous, effective minimum-dose treatment is recommended.

PPIs

These are pro-drugs, i.e., with the acid pH of the stomach, they are transformed by protonation into tetracyclic sulweds, which attach irreversibly to cysteine residues located on the periphery of the proton pump by forming bridges disulfides that block the pump for a long time.

The administration in the form of gastro-resistant micro-granules is mandatory for the molecules to reach their targets without experiencing protonation in gastric light.

It is best to take them in the morning if possible, on a fasting note, i.e., 30 minutes before the meal, which increases their efficiency by 30% compared to taking it during the meal.

Patients with GORs rarely have acidic gastric hypersecretion, but the typical acidity of the stomach is sufficient to cause peptic esophagitis.

The goal of an anti-secretory treatment during GOP is, therefore, to reduce the acidity of the gastric contents. This is especially important during the night when the food does not stamp the gastric acidity, and the patient is lying down. The long duration of action of the various anti-secretory drugs currently available allows this nocturnal inhibition of gastric secretion.

Antihistamines

These drugs work by blocking histamine's H2 receptors that stimulate acid secretion in the stomach.

The molecules currently existing are cimetidine, ranitidine, famotidine, and nizatidine.

Their effectiveness is less than that of PPIs, as only the histamine component is inhibited. As a general rule, their administration, preferably mono daily in the evening (maximum acid concentration at night and nocturnal acid secretion are blocked), is to continue for about 4 to 8 weeks. Their use is not recommended in case of kidney failure.

Cimetidine interferes with the oxidative metabolism of many drugs: its inhibitory effect on liver P450 cytochromes can reduce the metabolism of drugs normally detoxified by this enzyme system.

Prokinetics

They act on the pressure of the SIO to restore its competence. The most commonly used drugs are metoclopramide or domperidone. They can be used second-line, or in combination with anti-secretory drugs when symptoms remain common.

3. Surgical treatments

They are introduced when GERD is resistant to drug treatments, or in cases of anatomical abnormalities such as a hiatal hernia.

They are now often performed by coelioscopy. The results are satisfactory in 80 to 90% of cases.

The intervention takes place on the positioning of the SIO intra-abdominal with, if necessary, reduction of anatomical abnormalities (hiatal hernia, closure of the esophageal hiatus behind the esophagus by bringing the pillars of the diaphragm closer together and achieving anti-reflux mount).

The following organizational tree summarizes the classic path of management of a GOR, from its discovery to its functional exploration, ending with its drug or surgical treatment.

CHAPTER 4: GASTROESOPHAGEAL REFLUX AND PHYSICAL EXERCISE

The esophagus is a duct of about 25 cm, which carries food from the pharynx to the stomach. The esophagus flows into the stomach, into the abdominal cavity, and then through the diaphragm.

Under normal conditions, the organism prevents reflux through the lower esophageal or gastroesophageal sphincter, which is a few centimeters above the heart. This sphincter is physiological; that is, it is regulated by regulating the tone of the smooth musculature of the esophagus. The sphincter relaxes and opens during swallowing by the relaxation of the soft fibers.

The motility of the esophagus is controlled by reflexes directed through afferent and efferent fibers of the vagus nerve. The relaxation of the lower esophageal sphincter may also be related to innervation by fibers whose transmitting substance is nitric oxide. The IAS remains in tonic contraction until swallowing stimulates the peristaltic wave, and this wave reaches the sphincter, relaxes it, and allows the bolus to pass to the stomach.

Gastroesophageal reflux (GER) implies that the food bolus returns to the esophagus after it has already entered the stomach, through a retrograde flow. This is commonly due to transient or permanent changes in the mechanisms that naturally prevent stomach contents from returning to the esophagus. The causes may be an insufficiency of the lower esophageal sphincter (LES), transient relaxation of the lower esophageal sphincter, an alteration in the expulsion of gastric reflux from the esophagus, or a hiatus hernia.

Reflux can be considered to be a dysfunction of the lower esophageal sphincter, which is functionally responsible for maintaining esophageal pressure at a level higher than intragastric pressure, preventing the passage of gastric contents in the reverse direction. GER occurs when the IAS does not close properly, and stomach contents leak or reflux into the esophagus due to pressure difference. In healthy subjects, the LES maintains a hyper pressure zone of 15 to 20 mmHg above the stomach pressure, and this allows it to act as a barrier when the LES closes appropriately. Peristalsis of the esophagus may be reduced and ineffective, reduce amplitude, and insufficient for moving the bolus down and avoiding its rise. Although the main factor seems to be the relaxation of the LES, there is evidence that the marked decrease of peristalsis of the esophagus is associated with sphincter relaxation, apparently by neural inhibition.

Predisposing factors: Reflux can be triggered by factors such as:

- Obesity (especially abdominal obesity due to mechanical factors)
- Pregnancy
- Increased pressure intra-abdominal
- Lie down after food intake
- Hiatus Hernia
- High volumes of ingested food (gastric distention favors the relaxation of the LES)
- Certain foods such as chocolate, coffee or caffeinated tea, colas, and alcohol, which can irritate the esophagus and weaken the LES
- Use of belts or tight clothes
- Tobacco use can also undermine the IAS due to the release of B-adrenergic agents

Symptomatology:

- ***Epigastric burning:*** The gastric content has a very acidic pH, so it causes the burning sensation so intense when it rises into the esophagus
- ***Chest pain:*** Sometimes, you make a mistake with the ischemic pain of angina pectoris
- Painful lesions in the esophagus
- Bleeds in the esophagus
- Lasting cough (due to irritation of the esophagus since gastric juices can reach the mouth and then descend through the trachea and irritate the bronchi and cause cough as a reflex mechanism), and difficulty in swallowing (dysphagia)

- Bronchospasms (due to broncho-aspiration).

Bronchoaspiration is a severe consequence, which can lead to respiratory infections (expiratory pneumonia) or repeated episodes of bronchospasm. On the other hand, stomach acid progressively damages the wall of the esophagus in cases of chronic GER, developing Barrett's esophagus. This is characterized by metaplasia on the surface of the lower esophagus, where the simple high cylindrical epithelium replaces the normal stratified flat epithelium of the esophagus. This replacement is because the high single cylindrical epithelium is better prepared to resist gastric acids. This metaplasia represents an increased risk of future tumor developments, and It is considered a pre-malignant condition. It has been shown that the risk of Progress from an esophageal Barrett esophageal cancer increases significantly, in smokers compared to those who do not smoke, while the same relationship was found regarding alcohol consumption and body size. Barrett's esophagus is also characterized by ulcers in the wall of the esophagus, which are similar to gastric ulcers.

Other histopathological lesions of the esophagus may include isolated erosions, conclusive erosions, deep ulcers, and erythema. The esophagus can also become inflamed and reduce the light through which the bolus can pass through.

Hiatal hernia is a condition that favors reflux, and it occurs when a portion of the stomach travels through the diaphragmatic hiatus, from the abdominal cavity to the thorax. This abnormal location of the stomach causes external pressure to be exerted on the gastric content, and this promotes reflux.

The intake of high volumes of food can induce episodes of GER in the same way as its content because the distention of the proximal portion of the stomach activates receptors that distend the LES. If the intake of high volumes of food is done without dividing it into smaller intakes, there will be a decrease in the pressure of the IAS and an increase in reflux episodes in patients with GER, regardless of the content of the food, even if the diet is low in calories, if large volumes are consumed, relief will not be achieved symptomatic. All foods containing xanthines reduce the pressure of the IAS. Wine and alcohol reduce the weight of the IAS, cause an increase in the frequency and the duration of reflux, compared to water intake. It also decreases motility and esophageal peristalsis, contributing to reflux and heartburn.

Besides, a direct relationship between reflux and higher BMI has been demonstrated. Obesity and overweight significantly predispose the incidence of reflux, especially waist circumference. Epidemiologically, in cross-sectional studies, a clear relationship is shown between the high intake of fats in the diet and the frequency of occurrence of symptoms in patients with GER, although the mechanism is not fully known, and neither is the effects of ingestion. High fat affects, regardless of body weight.

Physical activity and nutrition can have favorable effects on GER, the indications to follow to prevent reflux is, most commonly, the following:

- Do not go to bed immediately after eating, wait, at least, 90 minutes
- Avoid the consumption of tobacco, alcohol, caffeine, chocolate, citrus fruits, sweets and fats, fried foods, and foods spiced with spices, alcohol, vinegar as they all significantly reduce the pressure of the IAS
- Avoid large intakes of both food and drinks. It is preferable to make smaller intakes so that the volume of stomach-filling is lower
- The volume of food at dinner should be moderate
- Avoid bowing with your head down, especially after eating
- Avoid abdominal efforts or exercises that increase intra-abdominal pressure, at least, for 3 hours after meals
- Avoid the use of abdominal girdles or clothes that are adjusted at the level of the abdomen
- Avoid constipation
- Raise the head of the bed by placing blocks of 10 to 15 centimeters.

The definitive treatment can also be pharmacological and surgical.

Proton pump inhibitors are usually used to decrease the production of acid in the stomach, thus prevent the esophagus from being seriously injured. But these inhibitors cannot be administered for a prolonged period since stomach acid is a critical defense against micro-organisms that can enter along with food, preventing food poisoning, and also necessary for the chemical degradation of food. Omeprazole and lansoprazole are examples of two drugs, symptoms of heartburn; you should consult the professional carefully before proton pump inhibitor, although they are effective in relieving their usage as they are also associated with several side effects. Moreover, antacids (sodium bicarbonate and magnesium salts), which are bases are used to increase the luminal gastric pH by neutralizing stomach acid and providing symptomatic relief for heartburn, although it doesn't treat the cause but only the symptom.

Sport or physical activity programs should be adapted in individuals with GER because the symptoms are related to the intensity and duration of the training, both long efforts, and high-intensity increase symptoms. Regarding the frequency of training or sessions, there has been no significant difference in the appearance of symptoms among those who do activity very frequently compared to those with a moderate frequency or a low frequency.Although it does seem there is a reduction in symptoms among those who regularly exercise intermediate. Probably, frequent training often favors the appearance of symptoms, and training infrequently does not allow the digestive system to adapt appropriately to exercise.

Because the parasympathetic nervous system primarily regulates the esophageal and digestive function, the intensity of an exercise has an inverse effect on the activity of the digestive system. That is, at higher concentrations of effort, the greater the predominant sympathetic-adrenal activity and Less is the parasympathetic activity at the gastrointestinal level. Parallel to this increased sympathetic activity, there is a redistribution of the peripheral circulation that manifests itself in the digestive system with vasoconstriction, lowering the irrigation of the entire area. However, it also seems that after a few minutes of vasoconstriction induced by the parasympathetic system, the flow can be recovered until almost normality using local metabolic vasodilator mechanisms that arose as a result of ischemia, being able to overcome the sympathetic effect and dilate the arterioles again (Guyton and Hall 2007). Sympathetic vasoconstriction is essential when other areas of the body need more significant contributions of blood, one of the most critical aspects of digestive vasoconstriction is that it allows a substantial reduction in the flow to the organs of digestion and splanchnic during short periods in cases of intense exercise.

Epidemiologically, it can be seen that most of the Alterations of the digestive system related to physical exercise are linked directly to the intensity of physical work. If the activity is of low or moderate intensity, it can have a positive effect on gastric emptying and intestinal transit. Still, if the intensity is high, the adrenal activity causes a slowdown of peristalsis and gastric emptying, increasing the risk of reflux. High-intensity exercise can facilitate the appearance of heartburn due to reflux and esophageal dysmotility:

Esophageal motility: There seems to be a significant decrease in the duration, amplitude, and frequency of esophageal contractions by increasing the intensity of effort (90% of Vo2 max). But with mild to moderate concentrations ($\leq$ 70% of Vo2 max by bicycle), this peristaltic function is improved. This shows that exercise has a powerful influence on esophageal motility and GER, in addition to increasing the exposure of the esophagus to gastric acid

Gastroesophageal reflux: Heartburn can be shared in intense endurance running exercises, and when monitoring the pH of the esophagus, it has been shown that GER frequently occurs about intense running physical exercise mainly, but also in a stationary bike. At high intensities (90% or more), the effects on esophageal function and the risk of reflux are similar in untrained individuals and athletes.

This is reinforced by knowing that in patients with GER, episodes of reflux are preceded by alterations in esophageal contractions and by a significant decrease in the frequency of contractions of the esophagus, as well as by relaxation of the LES.

This relaxation is also due to the same hormonal and nervous factors that influence the motility of the esophagus.

The answer to the question of what is the best option of physical activity for patients with GER is directly related to the intensity of the exercise, the type of exercise performed, and how is the diet in terms of quantity and content. It has been shown, as mentioned above, that high-intensity physical activity can alter the esophageal function and predispose to GER. Still, moderate or low-intensity exercise does not produce these effects and can be practiced without problems.

But other factors apart from the intensity, volume, and frequency of exercise should also be considered, such as the positions adopted in the exercises. The race has proved to be one of the exercises that induces the most reflux, while the exercise bike is much safer in this regard for those suffering from GERD probably due to the lower mechanical vibration of the body, without, however, one study found that weightlifters reported greater episodes of reflux than runners when evaluating athletes with reflux.

In one study, the incidence of reflux was compared in 25 middle-aged patients (35 years average) with GER who exercised in different positions, upright, inclined, and seated. Most of them suffered reflux in the forward lean exercises, which compress the abdomen, which increases intra-abdominal pressure and causes reflux. Those individuals who presented reflux when leaning forward from the standing and sitting position had lower pressure on the IAS. It is presumed that by increasing intra-abdominal pressure in individuals with decreased pressures of that sphincter...**THEN WHAT HAPPEN?**

Physiologically, there should be an increase in the pressure of the IAS as a response to the rise in the IAP due to maneuvers such as elevation of the legs from the supine position, inclination of the trunk, or the Valsalva maneuver to keep the pressure gradient between the esophagus and the stomach, this response, however, is deficient in patients with GER.

Exercises that can be recommended
As seen throughout the review, some important conclusions can be drawn to decide which physical activity is the most convenient:

- High-intensity exercises (90% of Vo2 max.) Have been shown to alter esophageal motility and favor the incidence of GER.
- Some foods have also been shown to alter the pressure of the IAS. So, avoid them before practicing physical exercise.

- Moderate exercise at low intensity (<70% of the Vo2 max) has shown not only to hinder esophageal activity but also to favor digestive function and intestinal transit.
- Patients with GER should limit the forward inclinations of the trunk that compress the abdominal region, or the Valsalva maneuver since the increase in pressure intra-abdominal favors reflux.
- A light meal that favors efficacious gastric emptying before an exercise session decreases the likelihood of reflux. You should not exercise intense physical after a hearty meal. Remember that high volumes of food predispose to the GER in the same way as the food content.
- GER should be treated to avoid severe injuries in the esophageal epithelium. Physical activity can help improve the quality of life and reduce body weight, which, in turn, helps in the treatment of GER.

CHAPTER 5: GASTROESOPHAGEAL REFLUX IN PREGNANCY

Bad taste in the mouth, abundant salivation, and a burning sensation in the throat, esophagus, and stomach. These are the symptoms of gastroesophageal reflux. Let's know more about this disorder.

It is a reasonably joint discomfort during pregnancy. The cause is that the gastric contents rise again into the esophagus. The esophagus is a 25-30 cm long canal that connects the mouth to the stomach. But why does it happen?

Causes of gastroesophageal reflux in pregnancy

The esophagus communicates with the stomach through the heart. Cardias is a muscular valve. It opens to allow the passage of food to the stomach and then closes again to prevent gastric juices from rising again. When, for any reason, the heart does not "work" well, the gastric content returns to the esophagus, and due to its acidity, irritates the mucosa that covers its walls. This causes a series of symptoms defined in medical terms such as heartburn. When this condition is repeated frequently and severely, there is the talk of gastroesophageal reflux disease.

During pregnancy, the heart does not work as it should for two reasons:

The first depends on the hormonal modifications of pregnancy. That is, it depends on the increase of progesterone, a hormone that relaxes the smooth muscles of the body. This also influences the musculature of the stomach, which empties more slowly, and as a consequence, even that of the heart, which tends to have less retention, allowing the gastric contents to pass backward.

To this reason is added another, typical of the last trimester of pregnancy, at which time the discomfort is usually accentuated. As the uterus grows and occupies more space in the abdominal cavity, it tends to push the stomach upwards. This organ, which is generally in an oblique position, is placed in a practically horizontal position. This modifies the correct anatomical orientation, and the hole of the cardias deforms and fails to close as it should. Such an incorrect position slows down the time taken to empty the stomach, keeping food in the stomach for longer and facilitating reflux.

Effective remedies against heartburn

Avoid large meals. Try to divide them into various snacks throughout the day. In this way, it prevents the stomach from becoming too full, which facilitates reflux.

Do not go to bed right after eating. Ideally, wait, at least, three hours. It will be necessary to organize, mainly if you are used to going to bed soon, ahead of dinner time. By not going to bed right after eating, the force of gravity will be used more as a means to favor the descent of food to the stomach, and therefore, digestion.

Avoid foods that require slow digestion (fried, processed or spicy foods, cured cheeses, and chocolate). Also, avoid those that stimulate gastric acidity (coffee, vinegar, alcohol, citrus, and tomato).

Chew slowly. The first digestion takes place in the mouth.

Pay attention also to soft drinks and chewing gum. Both increase the amount of air present in the stomach and encourage gastric juices to rise again.

Put something under the mattress to raise it so that you can avoid the fully stretched position.

Foods against heartburn in pregnancy

The heartburn in pregnancy, partly due to the hormonal revolution that is suffering. One of the functions of progesterone during pregnancy is to relax the muscles, so it also relaxes the stomach muscles. On the other hand, especially towards the end of pregnancy, the volume of the uterus-fetus set presses on the rest of the organs leaving little space.

Heartburn symptoms, particularly that burning sensation, are due to stomach juices rising from the pit of the stomach into the oesophagus. In parallel, other symptoms include gas, nausea, vomiting and a feeling of being fuller than humanly bearable, which makes the digestions extremely heavy and uncomfortable. In addition, during pregnancy, and due to the displacement of the organs, heartburn and heaviness can feel like discomfort or pain in the chest.

When the symptoms are severe, the use of antacids may be necessary, something that the doctor will prescribe. However, when the symptoms are mild, a change in diet or eating habits and even lifestyle may be sufficient to keep stomach acid under control.

- Cereals such as oats, rice or wheat (pasta or couscous), vegetables such as lettuce, green beans, broccoli or cauliflower, chicken and turkey meats or white fish, as well as fruits such as melon, watermelon or the banana can help relieve the symptoms of heartburn.

- Accompany meals with water, dispensing with other drinks.

- The milk can help control the acidity by neutralizing stomach acid. However, according to the latest studies, a rebound effect can occur, as it also stimulates acid production.

- Between hours you can have yoghurts or milkshakes and fruits, liquid foods and high in protein are usually easier to tolerate.

Other tips to avoid heartburn in pregnancy

- Avoid tobacco and alcohol. Pregnancy is reason enough to avoid them since they can cause damage to the fetus, but also, they make heartburn and heaviness worse.
- Limit caffeine (coffee, tea and colas), as it also makes symptoms worse.
- Eat slowly, regularly and small portions. Staying in an upright position after meals, to prevent gravity from helping gastric juices to rise into the oesophagus.
- Try not to eat before bedtime, better when they have already begun to digest food, at least 2-3 hours.
- Avoid triggers such as chocolate, juices, carbonated drinks, typically acidic foods, such as citrus fruits or tomatoes, and fatty foods.
- Avoid excessively spicy foods, especially spicy foods, although spices such as ginger seem to help improve symptoms.

Every woman is different, so it is advisable to make a list or keep a diary, pointing out foods that worsen and/or improve symptoms, because heartburn is something that can be repeated in future pregnancies.

Natural remedies to fight against acid reflux during pregnancy

Pineapple

The central stem of this fruit contains bromelain (this is an enzyme that reduces both the risk of inflammation and proteins and which promotes rapid healing of wounds). It has an action on the pH level in the small intestine and in the stomach. The results of animal studies have shown that this enzyme treats ulcers and heals the gastric mucosa. Bromelain also exists in tablet form.

The consumption of pineapple juice also helps to stop acid rising (indeed, this juice is very rich in enzymes). However, avoid consuming it too cold.

Baking soda

Baking soda neutralizes the acids present in the stomach, and its results are immediate (it should not be consumed regularly, but only when the pain becomes unbearable).
As soon as you feel pain, dissolve a teaspoon of baking soda in a glass of water and drink.

Vitamin d

Vitamin D plays a very important role in the treatment of infectious agents. When its level is optimally maintained, the body produces around 300 antimicrobial peptides (these effectively fight against all types of infections). The use of tanning booths and / or prolonged exposure to the sun can increase the level of vitamin D in the body. It is also possible to consume food supplements containing vitamin D (in this case, it is also necessary to increase its consumption of vitamin K2).

Ginger roots

With their gastro-protective properties, they help reduce acid production and suppress the Helicobacter pylori bacteria. The results of a study carried out in 2007 demonstrated that the roots of ginger are seven times more effective than Lansoprazole in combating gastric ulcers.

If you want to take advantage of its advantages, we advise you to prepare a ginger tea: add 3 or 4 pieces of roots in a glass of hot water. Let sit for 10 to 15 minutes, then drink (for optimal results, consume this preparation 20 minutes before meals).

Cinnamon

Although widely used for pastries, cinnamon has many medicinal properties: in addition to having a powerful antiseptic effect and to fight against the flu and colds, it also lowers the level of acid in the stomach. Here's how to use cinnamon: toast a piece of bread and butter it; afterwards, add raspberry jam and pour cinnamon and cardamom powder over it.

In order for the digestive juices present in your mouth to break down this food, we advise you to chew slowly and gently before swallowing.

Glutamine

It is an amino acid found in chicken, beef, eggs, dairy products, fish, and in some vegetables and fruits (it also exists in the form of tablets and capsules). The reports of a study published in 2009 have shown that it can treat the damage caused by the bacterium Helicobacter pylori (remember that it is responsible for the production of acid in the stomach).

Improvement after delivery

In general, heartburn tends to decrease after birth, since the two conditions caused it to decrease. Progesterone, which was produced, above all, by the placenta, suffers a steep declination with the expulsion of the latter. However, it will take a little more time (30-40 days) for the uterus to recover the same conditions as before pregnancy.

CHAPTER 6: 7 FOODS TO HELP WITH ACID REFLUX

Gastroesophageal reflux disease, known as GERD, is a digestive disorder where the stomach acid returns to the esophagus. This occurs when a valve known as the lower esophageal sphincter (IAS) is weakened or damaged.

It is a fairly common condition that affects approximately seven million people in the United States alone. And although there is no quick cure for GERD, eating certain foods can help with your symptoms by controlling the amount of acid the stomach produces, including these 7.

1. Vegetables

Due to their low fat and sugar content, vegetables are effective in reducing the amount of stomach acid that is produced. Almost all colors and varieties are beneficial, but "artichokes, green leafy vegetables, carrots, pumpkins, sweet potatoes, asparagus, green beans, peas, cucumber, and fennel" are especially important.

Health. Celery is also an excellent food option to combat acid reflux due to its high water content, such as parsley, which "has been used as a medicinal herb to calm the stomach and help digestion."

2. Ginger

Due to its natural anti-inflammatory properties, ginger is also considered useful in the treatment of heartburn and other digestive problems. This is because ginger "absorbs stomach acid and calms the nerve; this is because ginger "absorbs stomach acid and calms the nerves."

The source suggests eating it confit, drinking it in tea, or taking it as a supplement after a meal. Adding turmeric to your diet may also offer similar benefits.

3. Oatmeal

Not only is oatmeal a nutritious and abundant breakfast food, but it can also "absorb stomach acid and reduce reflux symptoms." A whole-grain diet offers an excellent source of fiber. It can "absorb acid in the stomach and reduce the symptoms of reflux." Whole-grain food provides an excellent source of fiber.

"Fiber in the diet has been linked to fewer symptoms of GERD," so you must consume an adequate amount. In addition to oatmeal, other sources of whole-grain fiber include brown bread and rice, as well as millet, quinoa, and couscous. "Fiber in the diet has been linked to fewer symptoms of GERD," so it is essential to make sure you consume an adequate amount. In addition to oatmeal, other sources of whole-grain fiber include brown bread and rice, as well as millet, quinoa, and couscous.

4. Non-citrus fruits

Many fruits are also an excellent source of fiber, as well as certain carbohydrates that are beneficial for reducing GERD symptoms. These include apples, berries, melons, bananas, peaches, and pears. These include apples, berries, melons, bananas, peaches, and pears.

Apples, in particular, can "reduce the amount of acid in the stomach and decrease the likelihood of reflux. However, Health.com notes that in a small percentage of cases (approximately 1 to 2 percent), bananas and melon can make a person's acid reflux worse. However, in a small percentage of cases (about 1 to 2 percent), bananas and melon can make a person's acid reflux worse.

5. fat-free meats

Because of their low-fat content, lean meats such as chicken, fish, and turkey can help reduce GERD symptoms. Trying them on the grill, grilled, baked, or poached.

Salmon, for example, is not only an excellent source of protein, but it also contains omega-3 fatty acids. Some have discovered that "adding omega-3 to their GERD diet significantly reduces GERD symptoms." However, this is not the case for everyone, so it is essential to consider your body's reaction after consuming it.

6. Egg whites

It has also been found that eggs reduce the symptoms of GERD, although you should "stay away from egg yolks, which are high in fat and can trigger symptoms of reflux."

Again, this is not the case for everyone, and some people worsen symptoms after eating egg whites, "which can trap air inside the GI tract."

7. healthy fats

While certain fats, such as saturated and trans fats, can make GERD symptoms worse, healthy fats can help mitigate them. A type of healthy fat is known as monounsaturated fats, which according to the International Foundation for Functional Gastrointestinal Disorders, come from sources such as olive oil, avocados, and a variety of nuts and seeds.

Polyunsaturated fats are another type, which according to the source, can be found in safflower, linseed, and nut oils; in soybean sources such as tofu, as well as in fatty fish such as salmon and trout.

Foods To Avoid For Acid Reflux
Acute acid reflux can be prevented by following the essential acid reflux diets below. Still, in chronic cases related to gastroesophageal reflux disease or GERD,

dietary treatment can only be useful to prevent acute exacerbations (outbreaks).

GERD is associated with SLE dysfunction (most common cause), as well as a hiatal hernia, increase intra-abdominal pressure, and delayed gastric emptying. Therefore, an acid reflux diet alone cannot treat GERD and must be incorporated along with medication for proper treatment.

It is known that certain foods decrease the tonicity of the esophageal sphincter (SLE). The integrity and proper functioning of the SLE are crucial to prevent stomach acid from flowing back into the esophagus. Other foods have been implicated in the increase of gastric acid that can contribute to acid reflux.

Foods and beverages that should be avoided include:

Beer

If you have gastric reflux, watch out for excess alcohol. Regular consumption of alcohol, such as beer, increases the risk of suffering from gastroesophageal reflux, according to a study. Heavy drinkers have an increased risk of developing this health problem.

The Orange juice

Particularly acidic, orange juice can worsen the symptoms of people with gastroesophageal reflux. In addition to increasing the acidity of the stomach, this drink is known to irritate the lining of the oesophagus. Choose less acidic juices like carrot juice.

Grapefruit

The Grapefruit is another citrus to avoid for people with gastric reflux. Highly acidic, this fruit can increase episodes of heartburn and regurgitation. In addition, it interacts with several drugs such as certain anti-inflammatory drugs and drugs against digestive disorders.

pineapple

Although pineapple contains bromelain, an enzyme with anti-inflammatory properties, some doctors advise patients with gastroesophageal reflux disease not to consume this tropical fruit. Why? Simply because pineapple is extremely acidic.

That said, you may not experience any symptoms when eating this fruit. If in doubt, consult your doctor, pharmacist or nutritionist.

Coffee

In some people, coffee causes gastric reflux. The culprit is caffeine, which helps relax the lower oesophagal sphincter, a muscle that prevents stomach contents from going back up into the oesophagus. When he is relaxed, the latter no longer does its job properly, which sometimes causes acid reflux.

Fizzy drinks

Generally rich in caffeine and carbon dioxide, two ingredients helping to reduce the tone of the lower oesophagal sphincter, carbonated drinks promote the appearance of gastroesophageal reflux. The best solution to stay hydrated is water, a safe drink for most people with gastric reflux.

Fried Chicken

The fried chicken may be delicious, but the high concentration of fat contributes to gastric reflux. Foods high in fat take longer to digest, which increases the risk of reflux.

To combat reflux, choose chicken without breading.

French fries

Whether or not you have gastroesophageal reflux, it is best that you closely monitor your consumption of fries. In addition to increasing the risk of mortality, this popular food in fast food chains promotes the appearance of gastric reflux. Very fatty, the fries stay longer in the stomach and weaken the lower oesophagal sphincter. These are two well-known causes of reflux.

Chocolate

Although it is one of the most popular foods in the world, chocolate has a bad press in people suffering from gastroesophageal reflux. The person responsible here would be the cocoa, of which the chocolate is partly made. Although this ingredient is antioxidant, it causes ingestion of a rise in serotonin levels, which tends to lower the tone of the lower oesophagal sphincter.

Spicy dishes

Are you a fan of spicy dishes? Be careful! Eating too spicy promotes the appearance of gastroesophageal reflux in some people by weakening the oesophagal sphincter in particular. In addition, researchers, as part of a study, linked the consumption of Korean spicy stews to the appearance of reflux.

The onions

It has long been known that onions, especially when raw, increase the risk of gastroesophageal reflux. This very popular vegetable in the kitchen is known to weaken the lower oesophagal sphincter and promote acid recovery.

To reduce the harmful effects of onions, cook them well and reduce your daily consumption.

Tomatoes

In some people, eating tomatoes increases the amount of stomach acid produced by the stomach. Too much stomach acid can end up causing heartburn and causing painful stomach reflux. Often a decrease in the consumption of tomatoes is enough to alleviate the symptoms. If in doubt, consult a doctor.

garlic

Garlic is generally not recommended for people prone to gastroesophageal reflux. This food, especially if eaten raw, can cause heartburn and increase episodes of gastric reflux.

Mint

Mint, whether fresh or in the form of candy or gum, is to be avoided if you wish to combat gastric reflux. The volatile acids contained in this plant reduce the tone of the lower oesophagal sphincter, which increases the risk of acid rising in the oesophagus.

Cow's milk

The cow's milk may cause gastric reflux, especially in people with an intolerance or allergy to cow's milk. If you suffer from reflux, try, with your doctor's agreement, cow's milk substitutes such as soy, almond or rice milk.

Red meat

Are you a meat lover? Try to limit your consumption of red meat as much as possible. In addition to being fatty, red meat is a food that takes time to digest. Long digestion forces the stomach to remain swollen longer, creating increased pressure on the lower oesophagal sphincter.

Peppermint tea

If peppermint tea is a popular digestive, people prone to gastric reflux should be wary of it. Peppermint acts as a relaxant on the lower oesophagal sphincter. No longer being fully operational, the latter has difficulty in stopping acid lifts.

Frozen pizza

With its tomato sauce and fatty cheese, it's no wonder that frozen pizza causes gastroesophageal reflux. This processed food is also linked to other complications of the digestive system, such as Barrett's oesophagus (a precancerous condition caused in particular by chronic gastric reflux) and cancer of the oesophagus.

Cold meats

Many cold slices of meat contain a large amount of fat, which promotes the onset of symptoms of gastroesophageal reflux. For healthier lunches, choose less fatty meats such as turkey.

Wine

The wine by its acidity and concentration of alcohol increases, in some people, the amount of acid produced by the stomach. Too much stomach acid increases the risk of experiencing gastric reflux.

Studies indicate that red wine is a better option for people experiencing gastroesophageal reflux. If in doubt, consult your doctor.

Consider a diet restricted in calories and low in GI (glycemic index). While this type of food may not directly affect acid reflux, it is crucial for weight loss, which is essential in the treatment of GERD.

Heartburn: 15 natural remedies that work

Temporary heartburn is often mild - but very painful. This painful burning sensation behind the sternum occurs when the very aggressive stomach acid rises in the oesophagus, which can happen, for example, after a large meal.

To preserve your health - and your stomach - it may be best not to rush to drugs right away, but to find a natural remedy to relieve heartburn. But then, what are Grandma's remedies that are really effective against stomach reflux and heartburn? We investigated!

To start, let's be clear: THE grandmother's remedy for heartburn ... does not exist. What works for one person doesn't necessarily work for another. Everyone has to find out which remedy relieves their symptoms.

But some natural remedies and grandmother's tricks have been proven to work in large numbers of people with mild heartburn. Do not hesitate to test one - or more - of the following propositions! Hopefully, they will work for you too!

Natural remedy n ° 1: Soothing herbal teas

Herbal teas are a well-known grandmother's remedy for relieving heartburn. Certain mixtures of herbs and plants have been shown to be particularly effective, such as chamomile, fennel, anise, cumin, yarrow.

Remember: liquorice infusion also helps relieve heartburn. However, it should not be consumed over an extended period.

Natural remedy n ° 2: Nuts and almonds

Here is a piece of good advice against heartburn: slowly chew a few almonds or nuts, then swallow the "porridge". It is not very glamorous, but it seems that it works!

Natural remedy n ° 3: Raw potatoes

Potatoes are known for their diuretic, calming and healing action. But did you know that the potato is a real natural antacid?

Also, the juice of raw potatoes is often advised to relieve gastric ailments such as ulcer, constipation, gastric acidity, heartburn,...

Drinking raw potato water before a meal would neutralize excess stomach acid. Some also recommend drinking the cooking water from the potatoes... It's your turn!

Natural remedy n ° 4: Chewing gum

Sugar-free chewing gum is your sweetie? So much, the better! Because chewing increases the production of saliva, which in turn neutralizes stomach acid.

But beware: if you tend to suffer from bloating, chewing gum is not recommended!

Natural remedy n ° 5: Do not go to bed with a full stomach!

To prevent heartburn, it is advisable not to go to bed with a full stomach, that is, just after the evening meal. Ideally, you should eat at least 3 hours before bed...

Natural remedy # 6: sleep in the right position

The gastroesophageal reflux disease (GERD) are favoured by the elongated position. Also, to prevent heartburn, it is advisable to sleep while raising your upper body to reduce the risk of acid going up into the oesophagus.

If you like to sleep on your side, avoid lying on your right side! Why? The stomach is located on the left side of our body. When you are lying on the left side, the stomach is therefore located lower than the oesophagus, which reduces the symptoms of acid reflux...

Natural remedy n ° 7: Monitor your diet

It is rather a bit of lifestyle advice than a grandmother's remedy, but it is often effective: Watch your diet to check if certain foods systematically cause heartburn in you. Once you have identified these foods, you can reduce their consumption or even replace them with others.

Here are some foods often involved in heartburn:

- fatty foods and fried foods,

- citrus and fruit juices,

- fizzy drinks,

- strong spices like chilli, pepper or curry,

- the dried fruit,

- smoked food,

- spearmint and peppermint,

- the bread fresh,

- the milk ,

Note: not all people with heartburn react to all of these foods (luckily!). It's up to you to test which food (s) your stomach supports well or not...

And don't forget: if the stomach can react sensitive to certain foods, it can also feel stressed by stress! So don't hesitate to slow down if you feel the stress mounting. Your stomach will thank you!

Also, watch out for certain "pleasure" foods that stimulate the secretion of gastric acids!

In case of heartburn are therefore to be avoided:

- alcoholic beverages,

- the tea (black)

- the coffee,

- milk chocolate,

Obviously, if you find that your stomach reacts badly to one of these products, you should limit it to consumption.

Stop smoking!

Cigarettes aggravate heartburn because it has a direct action on the gastric mucosa and tends to increase gastric acidity ... So avoid!

Natural remedy n ° 8: Take the time to eat!

Again, this is more advice than a remedy to avoid gastric reflux: eat slowly and "mindful", taking the time to chew each bite.

It is also better to split your meals (4 to 6 meals a day) rather than focusing on 2 or 3 "large" meals, on one side to facilitate digestion, and on the other side to avoid arriving hungry for meals and serving themselves too much...

Also, make sure you choose the right cooking method: avoid frying and prefer steamed or simmered preparations.

Natural remedy # 9: plain water above all

Soft drinks can cause heartburn in people with sensitive stomachs. So with the adored soda, prefer a glass of still water, or a fruit juice diluted with water...

Natural remedy n ° 10: Physical activity

It's a fact: people with regular physical activity suffer less from stomach problems like heartburn.

Natural remedy # 11: slow down and listen

Here is the most economical and lasting remedy for heartburn: do NOTHING, or rather, relax!

And yes, often, the stress and the agitation of our hectic life can literally "weigh on the stomach". Listen to your body and do yourself good, for example, by taking regular breaks. Relaxation techniques or meditation can also help!

Natural remedy # 12: comfortable clothes

Clothing that is too tight, such as a belt that is too tight, increases the pressure on the abdominal region, and thus the risk of suffering from heartburn.

Natural remedy n ° 13: Pay attention to the weight

In some cases, losing weight can help decrease or prevent heartburn in the long run.

Of course, this is not about making a special "anti-gastric burn" diet! But you should know that being overweight increases the pressure in the stomach and in the oesophagus, which can hamper the proper functioning of the sphincter between the stomach and oesophagus. However, the reduction of the closing mechanism of this passage promotes gastric reflux and heartburn.

Natural Remedy # 14: The Symptoms Journal

While keeping a symptom log is not really a cure in itself, it can help identify the causes of your heartburn.

In this log, you can write down information like:

- when did you have heartburn

- in what situation were you (stress, fatigue, ...)

- what did you eat and drink that day?

These indications will allow you to identify the possible factors triggering your heartburn. If your journal says, for example, that alcohol consumption may be causing your stomach reflux, take a quick test and give up alcohol for a while to see if the heartburn goes away or goes away.

Be warned: finding THE triggers may require a little patience. Also, it is possible that you cannot clearly identify the precise cause of your disorders ... But the effort is worth it.

Natural remedy n ° 15: Medicines

When no grandmother's remedy works for your heartburn, go to a pharmacy for advice. There are low-dose, over-the-counter medications available that can relieve your symptoms.

Please note: these drugs are not intended for long-term or long-term treatment. If these over-the-counter medications don't work, you should seek medical attention!

When to consult a doctor?

Grandma remedies for heartburn ... it's good, but they have their limits.

You should definitely consult a doctor if:

● symptoms are recurrent or

● if heartburn lasts more than two weeks.

A visit to the doctor is also indicated in the presence of secondary symptoms such as:

● blood in the stool, black urine

● net weight gain, with no apparent

● strong abdominal cramps, lasting pain, swelling in the abdominal region

● swallowing difficulties

● diarrhoea,

● vomiting, coughing up blood.

Finally, if you have ever suffered from a stomach ulcer or duodenum, you should also consult a doctor in case of heartburn.

CHAPTER 7: BREAKFAST RECIPES

Nutrition Plan for Reflux: What to look for?

Many people find it difficult to identify those having a positive effect on reflux among a variety of foods. Reflux refers to the pathological reflux of acid gastric juice into the esophagus. This usually does not happen because a barrier between the esophagus and the stomach ensures that gastric juice cannot pass through. What does an optimal nutrition plan for reflux look like? What can be eaten during the day, for example? Which foods are better, which ones less? This article deals with these questions exactly.

What could the nutritional plan for reflux look like?

For breakfast, it is especially a warm porridge. This can be prepared from oat flakes, but also millet or buckwheat flour. The desired cereal is infused with hot water to the grain as it begins to swell. The porridge can be refined with fruit. These include, for example, a homemade fruit mousse, a grated apple, or a handful of berries. For pancake lovers, pancakes and buckwheat flour with fruit are also recommended.

For the main meals, vegetables and salad of every kind should be on the nutritional plan as often as possible. A gourd-ginger soup, for example, fills up the base deposits of the body. Furthermore, a potato-vegetable gratin can be baked, or a salad with lean turkey strips is served. Valuable cereal with vegetables and tasty herbs is a change in the nutritional plan. Importantly, the diet should include around 80% basic and 20% acid foods to counteract reflux through a balance between acids and bases. Vegetables and lettuce offer a variety of bases, making it possible to consume small amounts of acidic foods, as the base-feeding foods compensated them.

Reflux disease is widespread in the world. Unfortunately, many people suffer from the typical symptoms of heartburn, acid regurgitation, or burning in the stomach. Reflux can be asymptomatic for a long time, but it is essential to treat it to minimize long-term damage and consequences. The constant irritation of the mucous membrane in the esophagus can lead to inflammation, which, in turn, can lead to malignant changes. Given the multitude of different foods, it does not seem illogical that there is an overwhelming amount of foods that should be consumed to relieve reflux symptoms. This chapter deals with choosing the right foods and tips for recipes.

1. Spelled bread without yeast

ingredients For 1 portion

500 gSpelled flour, type 630

½ TLsalt

½ literWater, lukewarm

1 teaspoonBread spice mix

1 pck.Cream of tartar

100 glinseed
100 gpumpkin seeds

Olive oil for the baking dish

Preparation

Working time approx. 10 minutes

Cooking/baking time approx. 1 hour

Total time approx. 1 hour 10 minutes

1. Mix the flour with the tartar powder. Then mix in salt, bread spice, flax seeds, and pumpkin seeds. Finally, add the lukewarm water and knead by hand.
2. Grease a box mold with a little olive oil and fill in the dough. Brushing the surface of the dough with a little water will make it nice and crispy.
3. Place in the cold oven and bake at 200 ° C top/bottom heat for 60 minutes.
4. The same dough can also be used for delicious spelled rolls, for example, with sunflower seeds.

2. Puff pastry - quiche with broccoli and camembert vegetarian and basic

ingredients For six portions

1 pck. Puff pastry from the refrigerated shelf

600g Broccoli or cauliflower, chard or spinach

200g Camembert
200ml cream
1 pinch nutmeg
2 Egg
salt and pepper

Preparation

Working time approx. 1 hour

Total time approx. 1 hour

1. Lay out the puff pastry in a springform pan. Preheat the oven to 180°C convection. Wash the broccoli and cut into small florets.
2. Put some water in a saucepan, add the broccoli and cook for about 5 minutes over medium heat. Drain in a sieve, drain and distribute on the dough. Cut the cheese into thin slices and decoratively lay on the broccoli.
3. Whisk the cream with eggs and spices and pour over the broccoli and cheese. Then bake on the middle rail about 40 - 45 minutes golden yellow.
4. If you like, you can replace the broccoli with other vegetables (e.g., fresh leaf spinach - but then 1 kg, chard, or cauliflower). If you do not like camembert, you can also take feta cheese, then the quiche gets

a very different note, and the dish is nevertheless fundamental. This fits a basic salad with lemon dressing.

3. Muesli basic mix

also for basic nutrition

Ingredients For 1 portion

- 20 gSugar, brown
- 70 ghoney
- 2 Teaspoons sesame oil
- ½Vanilla pod (n)
- 1 teaspoonground cinnamon
- 250 goatmeal
- 20 gsesame
- 50 gAlmond(s), chopped
- 50 gAlmond(s), planed
- 50 gSunflower seeds

Preparation

Working time approx. 20 minutes

Cooking/baking time approx. 15 minutes

Total time approx. 35 minutes

1. Scrape out the vanilla pod. In a large saucepan, heat sugar, honey, sesame oil, cinnamon, and the pith of

the vanilla pod together with the vanilla pod at a low temperature until the sugar has melted. Remove the vanilla pod. Evenly submerge the oatmeal, sesame seeds, and sunflower seeds. This may take a little longer but stir, gain and again, toss the sugar from the wooden spoon and fold again until everything is well mixed. Spread the mixture on a baking sheet lined with baking paper, place in the oven, and bake at 175 ° C for approx. 7 minutes, depending on the type of stovetop. Sprinkle the chopped and sliced almonds over and bake for about 7 minutes until the mass becomes slightly brownish and smells pleasant.

2. Allow it to cool on the tin and place it in a tin.
3. If necessary, mix with yogurt and dry or fresh fruit.

Tip:

The recipe can be modified with pumpkin seeds, hazelnuts, etc.

4. Spelled bread with sunflower seeds
Basic bread recipe

ingredients For 1 portion

• 500 gSpelled flour, type 1050

• 250 gSpelled flour, type 630

- •½ tbsp. salt
- •¾ liter Water, lukewarm
- •250 gSunflower seeds, or others
- •1 teaspoonBread spice mix
- •2 pck.Cream of tartar
- •Oil (coconut), or other oil for the mold

Preparation

Working time approx. 10 minutes

Cooking/baking time approx. 45 minutes

Total time approx. 55 minutes

1. First, mix all dry ingredients and then pour in the lukewarm water, knead well with a dough hook.
2. Please do not be surprised; the dough is looser (tough-tearing) than usual.
3. Grease a box mold. Pour in the dough, dab the dough surface with a little water to make the crust nice and crispy.
4. Bake in a preheated oven at 200 degrees for 30 minutes. During the first 30 minutes slide on the middle rail, and the last 15 min. on the lowest so that the bread is not too dark.
5. Since I have a small baking dish, I fill the remaining dough in Muffinförmchen and have it in 25 minutes, super delicious, freshly baked small rolls.

5. Fruit buckwheat porridge with pomegranate seeds
vegan, basic

Ingredients For 2 portions

- 100 gbuckwheat
- 2 Bulb
- Banana
- Apple
- 1 handful raisins
- 2 Teaspoons of Sweet lupine flour, optional
- 2 Teaspoons of Almond butter
- 2 Teaspoons of lemon juice
- 100 ml of Almond milk (almond drink)
- Pomegranate

Preparation

Working time approx. 20 minutes

Resting time approx. 2 days

Cooking/baking time approx. 4 hours

Total time approx. 2 days 4 hours 20 minutes

1 Soak the buckwheat in water for 1 hr, pour into a colander, rinse off, and allow to stand in the colander over a bowl to germinate, rinsing under running water in the morning and evening. Buckwheat germinates after 1 - 2 days (it then becomes alkaline, has more nutrients, and is more compatible) and can be further processed.

2 Distribute 3 - 4 tablespoons of germinated buckwheat on a baking sheet and let it circulate in the oven at approx. 50°C circulating air for approx. 3 - 4 hours. If you have a dehydrator, of course, you better take this.

3 Add the remaining buckwheat to the blender with raisins, sweet lupine flour, almond paste, lemon juice, and almond milk. Core the pears and apple. Peel the banana. Add the fruit as well. Everything about 90 seconds, and mix well. If the porridge is too firm, add some almond milk, but not too much, it should not be liquid.

4 Distribute the fruit pulp on two cereal bowls.

5 Remove the pomegranates from the pomegranate and add to the ingredients. Allow the dried buckwheat grains to cool slightly and then distribute them on top.

Notes:

The sweet lupine flour can be omitted, but it is an excellent source of protein.

Instead of almond paste, you can also use the almond pomace, which is leftover when making almond milk.

6. Buckwheat semolina

Basic and vegan

Ingredients For two portions

- 400 ml of coconut milk

- 200 ml Almond milk (almond drink), unsweetened

- 100 gSemolina (buckwheat semolina)

- 1 handful of your choice fruit, preferably fresh

Preparation

Working time approx. 15 minutes

Total time approx. 15 minutes

1 Boil the coconut and almond milk in a saucepan. Remove the pot from the heat and stir in the buckwheat semolina.

2 Fill the semolina pudding into dessert bowls, allow to cool slightly and enjoy with fresh fruit.

7. Maroni coconut cream "Symphony of the trees."

Basic, gluten-free, vegan

Ingredients For 1 portion

- 2 tbspChestnut flour or chestnut raw food powder
- 100 mlCoconut milk, up to 200 ml
- 1 shotwater
- 1 pinchsalt
- 1 tbspAlmond butter
- 1 handfulFruit, cut small, depending on the season
- 1 teaspooncinnamon

Preparation

Working time approx. 15 minutes

Total time approx. 15 minutes

1 Strain the chestnut raw food powder/flour with the dash of water and salt. If you prefer the ayurvedic variant, this can still heat up.

2 Put this porridge on a deep plate, add warm coconut milk (about 100 - 200 ml), and cut fruit. On top of that, add almond paste and cinnamon.

8. A dark chocolate cream with figs
Simple, basic, with no added sugar

Ingredients For 1 portion

- 50 g Fig (s), dried
- 25 ml of water
- ground cinnamon
- 5 g Cocoa powder, slightly de-oiled
- 10 g cream

Preparation

Working time approx. 5 minutes

Rest time approx. 1 hour

Total time approx. 1 hour 5 minutes

1 Chop the figs very small and add half as much water, in this case, 25 ml. Stir well and leave to soak for an hour.

2 Now, add the cocoa powder, the cinnamon at will, and the cream and stir well.

3 I like to eat this cream on bread, or in pancakes.

4 This recipe can vary in many ways. Instead of figs, take dried dates, vanilla pods, or ground nuts.

9. Apple and coconut cream
Vegan, basic, gluten-free, and GAT-fair

Ingredients For 2 portions

- 360 g Apfelmark
- 4 TL, heaped Brown millet, ground
- 2 tablespoons, heaped Erdmandelflocken
- 1 teaspooncinnamon
- 1 tbsp lemon juice
- 250 gYoghurt (coconut milk yogurt), vegan, gluten-free

Preparation

Working time approx. 5 minutes

Total time approx. 5 minutes

1 Put all ingredients in a bowl and stir.

10. Apple and almond muesli mandarins
Basic and delicious

Ingredients For 2 portions

- apples
- 2 tbspAlmond, planed
- 3 tbspWalnuts, chopped
- 2 tbspTigernut (Tigernut Chufas Nüssli)

- 2 tbspCranberries

- Mandarine

Preparation

Working time approx. 10 minutes

Total time approx. 10 minutes

1. Squeeze out the tangerines and put the juice in a bowl. Peel, quarter, core and grate the apples, add to the juice and stir. Add almonds, walnuts, Chufas-Nüssli, and cranberries.

11. Danny's morning hour - basic breakfast buffet
vegan

Ingredients For 2 Portions

- tbsp Millet, or double the amount already popped or ground, see instructions

- tbsp Buckwheat, or twice the amount already popped or ground, see instructions

- 250 ml Almond milk (almond drink) or oat milk (oat drink)

- 1 tbsp Amaranth, puffed or half puffed, and then puff it yourself, see instructions

- 1 tbsp Sunflower seeds

- 1 tbsp pumpkin seeds

- 1 tbsp Almond (s), whole

- 1 Apple

- 2 tbsp Pineapple pieces, frozen

Preparation

Working time approx. 10 minutes

Cooking/baking time approx. 3 minutes

Total time approx. 13 minutes

1. Put 2 tablespoons of millet and buckwheat into a Flocker or a flour mill and flake or grind. I always use the Flocker. Those who do not have both should buy flakes in the organic market. It then takes about twice the amount as flakes.

2. Put in a saucepan 250 ml of almond milk or similar liquid that you like. In the cold liquid, stir the flakes. Boil the almond milk while stirring and continue to stir until the porridge has the desired consistency. This usually takes only 1 - 2 minutes. Remove the pot from the heat and add the tablespoon of popped Amaranth. In a good blender (for smoothies), pour the chopped apple, the frozen pineapple pieces, the sunflower and pumpkin seeds, and almonds with a dash of water. Stir the mixture into the porridge.

Tips and advice:

Instead of almond milk, go for oat milk, rice drink (very sweet) or water, and if you like milk, you can also use these.

If you have only unpopped amaranth, then you can pop it. To do this, dry a small ceramic pan on the stove at the highest level. Have a small lid ready to fit on the pan. Now, put a maximum of half a tablespoon of amaranth into the pan, put the lid on it, lift the pan immediately from the cooking area, and swing it through until the amaranth is popped. But you can also grind the amaranth in a flour mill and boil it together with the millet and buckwheat. I've already flocked the amaranth, but then you usually have hard balls in the pulp.

Instead of a smoothie mixer, you can also chop the nuts and seeds with any other suitable machine and make a smoothie with pineapple, apple, and a dash of water using a blender.

If you like, you can add a dash of linseed oil or use any other frozen or fresh fruit instead of apple and pineapple. The porridge also tastes good with banana and mango or with raspberries.

I also like to add one tablespoon chia seeds to the porridge before cooking, but then take a little more liquid. This can still stir after cooking when the porridge becomes too firm.

12. Basic breakfast buffet with buckwheat

Apple, carrot, banana, and buckwheat make a great breakfast!

Ingredients For 2 people

- Organic apple 2 pieces/200g
- carrots 2 pieces/120g
- Banana/n 1 piece/110g
- Buckwheat flour 50 grams
- water 400 grams
- Rapeseed oil (native) 1 tablespoon/12g
- walnuts 3 tablespoons/30g
- salt 1 pinch/n/1g

Preparation

1. Boil the water with a pinch of salt. Wash buckwheat semolina with hot running water in a strainer. Remove the pot from the heat, add the buckwheat semolina and simmer over low heat while stirring for about 5 minutes.
2. In the meantime, wash the carrots and apple, peel and finely grate. Crush banana. Anyone who wants to can put everything together with the oil.
3. Stir the fruit – carrot mixture and the oil in the still warm breakfast porridge. Fill the basic breakfast

porridge with buckwheat semolina into two small bowls and serve. Bon Appetit!

13. Basic cereal

Basic breakfast with buckwheat for a healthy start to the day

Ingredients For two people

- millet grains 20 grams

- buckwheat 50 grams

- pumpkin seeds 30 grams

- Sunflower seeds 30 grams

- hazelnuts 30 grams

- Date 3 pieces/15g

- Organic apple 1 piece/120g

- cinnamon something/1g

- water 400 grams

Preparation

1. Crush buckwheat, millet, seeds, and nuts with a suitable kitchen appliance, e.g., a powerful smoothie maker.

2. Cut the dates and the fig into the smallest possible pieces.
3. Boil all shredded basic foods with approx. 400 ml of water and turn the temperature down for 3 minutes.
4. In the meantime, peel an apple or another basic fruit (e.g., banana) and peel it into bite-sized pieces.
5. Remove the basic muesli from the heat, allow to cool slightly, stir in apple and cinnamon and serve. Bon Appetit!

Note: The basic muesli can also be prepared in advance for simply preparing larger quantities without fresh fruit and keeping them airtight. The basic muesli mixture lasts for several weeks.

Nutritional information

per serving per 100g

Kilojoules (calories)1808 (432)   520 (124)

protein 15.45 g   4.44 g

carbohydrates44.43 g   12.77 g

fat 21.27 g   6.11 g

fructose 11.10 g   3.19 g

sorbitol 0.25 g   0.07 g

glucose 8.43 g   2.42 g

lactose content0.00 g   0.00 g

14. Fruit salad with strawberries and tiger nuts

Very healthy, a basic breakfast

ingredients For 4 people

- apples 2 pieces / 220g

- strawberries 250 grams

- blueberries 80 grams

- Kiwi /s 2 pieces / 160g

- orange juice 150 milliliters

- Orange / 1 piece / 150g

- Erdmandelflocken 200 grams

Preparation

1. Peel the apples and prepare on a grater in small pieces or Mus. Chop the remaining fruit and put everything in a bowl.
2. Mix the orange juice with the Chufas Nüssli (strawberry flakes) and let it swell briefly. Then combine everything.
3. A purely basic breakfast!

Nutritional information

	per serving	per 100g
Kilojoules (calories)	1521 (363)	503 (120)
protein	4.15g	1.37 g
carbohydrates	54.35g	17.97 g
fat	13.23g	4.37 g
fructose	12.84g	4.24 g
sorbitol	0.25 g	0.08 g
glucose	9.40 g	3.11 g
lactose content	0.00 g	0.00 g

15. Millet and soymilk porridge for gourmets

Breakfast recipe with iron-containing foods

ingredients for two people

- millet 120 grams
- soy milk 280 grams
- sugar syrup 20 grams
- Almond butter 1 tablespoon / 12g
- lemon juice Splashes / 2g
- raspberries 40 grams
- salt 1 pinch / 1g

Preparation

1. Wash the millet with hot water and then boil for 5 minutes in the soymilk.
2. Add the almond purée, sugar beet syrup, lemon juice, and a pinch of salt, and let it swell for another 10 minutes.
3. The porridge is reminiscent of rice pudding. It tastes warm and tasty with fruits. The vitamin C in the fruits is also good in iron deficiency so that the iron of millet and sugar beet syrup can be better absorbed. However, it tastes excellent even without fruit. Visually, it looks a bit greyish because of the sugar beet syrup. But it makes it very tasty and ironier. Be sure to use soy milk without adding calcium, as calcium hinders iron absorption.

Nutritional information

per serving per 100g

Kilojoules (calories)1399 (334) 589 (141)

protein 12.41 g 5.23 g

carbohydrates   51.14 g 21.53 g

fat   8.05 g 3.39 g

fructose 5.33 g 2.25 g

sorbitol 0.00 g 0.00 g

glucose 5.28 g 2.22 g

lactose content0.00 g   0.00 g

16. Green Curry Coconut Avocado Soup
Cold appetizer - very healthy

ingredients For 4 people

- Avocado / s 2 pieces / 300g

- coconut milk 0.5 can / 200g

- curry 1 teaspoon / 4g

- Vegetable broth (gluten-free) 600 milliliters

- lemon juice 3 tablespoons / 25g

- salt 1 teaspoon / 5g

- pepper 1 pinch / n / 1g

Preparation

1. Free the medium-ripe avocados from the core and peel and place in a blender.
2. Add the vegetable stock and mix until it's well blended.
3. Then add the coconut milk, curry, lemon juice, salt, and pepper, and mix until a creamy liquid is formed.
4. Now, taste it and cool if necessary. The soup can also be enjoyed at room temperature. Bon Appetit!

Nutritional information

per serving   per 100g

Kilojoules (calories)1005 (242) 354 (85)

protein 2.33 g 0.82 g

carbohydrates5.86 g 2.06 g

fat   23.26 g 8.20 g

fructose 0.59 g 0.21 g

sorbitol 0.00 g 0.00 g

glucose3.34 g 1.18 g

lactose content   0.00 g 0.00 g

17. Parsnip Soup
Lactose-free, gluten-free, egg-free, dairy-free

ingredients For 4 people

•Parsnip 3 pieces / 600g

•Vegetable broth (yeast-free, gluten-free, without glutamate) 1 liter / 1000g

•salt 1 gram

•Celery (fresh) 50 grams

•Tomatoes (tin) 150 grams

•Onion 1 piece / 150g

- Laurel leaves (dried) 1 piece / 1g

- Parsley (fresh) something / 10g

Preparation

1. The parsnips are cleaned and then cut into small pieces.
2. Now, cut the onion and celery into small cubes. Add the Geschnibbelte in the broth and bring to a boil, as a seasoning nor a bay leaf. Now, cook everything for 30 minutes.
3. Add the peeled canned tomatoes after 20 minutes and cook for 10 minutes.
4. After cooking, remove the bay leaf and puree the soup (blender/blender).
5. Add salt, pepper, and parsley as you like, and if you like it spicy, you may add a little more. Of course, you can experiment with other spices as you like. In case of light diet, season carefully, and if necessary, omit the onion. Bon Appetit!

Nutritional information

per serving per 100g

Kilojoules (calories)660 (157)134 (32)

protein3.59 g 0.73 g

carbohydrates   22.50 g 4.59 g

83

fat   5.47 g 1.11 g

fructose 4.15 g 0.85 g

sorbitol 0.00 g 0.00 g

glucose 4.23 g 0.86 g

lactose content 0.00 g 0.00 g

18. Colorful Ratatouille

Ideal for a base cure or to lose weight!

ingredients For 2 people

•Aubergine 1 piece / 340g

•Tomatoes 3 pieces / 150g

•Zucchini / s 1 piece / 210g

•Vegetable broth (yeast-free, gluten-free, without glutamate) 150 milliliters

•olive oil 3 tablespoons / 25g

•sea-salt 3 pints / n / 3g

•Thyme (fresh) 5 grams

•Onion 1 piece / 50g

Preparation

1. Cut the zucchini and aubergine into small pieces. Cover the tomatoes with boiling water, leave to stand, and peel off the skin. The tomatoes are eighth.
2. Chop half the onion and fry in olive oil. Add zucchini and aubergine and sauté. Add the 150 ml vegetable stock and add the tomatoes — season with salt and herbs. Cook for approximately 10 minutes and serve.

Note: Sea salt should always be used for a base cure!

Nutritional information

per servingper 100g

Kilojoules (calories)   830 (198)   178 (43)

protein5.54 g   1.19 g

carbohydrates10.53 g   2.26 g

fat   14.75 g   3.16 g

fructose 4.93 g   1.06 g

sorbitol 0.19 g   0.04 g

glucose 4.67 g1.00 g

lactose content   0.00 g0.00 g

19. Green smoothie with avocado, cucumber, and salad

Detox smoothie recipe with lots of vegetables - very healthy

ingredients For 3 people

- Orange 1 piece / 140g
- Apple 1 piece / 120g
- Avocado / s 0.5 pieces / 90g
- n cucumber / 1 piece / 350g
- Spinach leaves (frozen) 100 gram
- Parsley (fresh) 40 grams
- Lamb's lettuce 100 gram
- Sunflower seeds 2 tablespoons / 15g
- Linseed (ground / gluten-free) 2 tablespoons / 15g
- water 150 milliliters

Preparation

1. Flax seeds and sunflower seeds in a cup together with a little water.
2. Peel avocado. Wash cucumber, lettuce, parsley, and put all ingredients in the blender.
3. Peel the orange with the knife and cut it into two or three pieces. This is faster than carefully peeling them off with your hands. The orange will be mashed soon anyway.

4. Wash the apple, core (do not peel) and cut into small pieces.
5. Blend everything for about 1 minute with the blender (which should have, at least, 800 watts + 1.5 liters).
6. The amount is sufficient with the specified amount of water for three large glasses á 0.3 liters and is quite viscous. The smoothie should, therefore, be served with a spoon. The amount of water can also be varied for those who like it more fluid. Even apple juice can be added, but then increases the fructose content.

Nutritional information

per serving   per 100g

Kilojoules (calories)681 (163) 183 (44)

protein   6.33 g 1.70 g

carbohydrates16.35 g 4.38 g

fat 7.53 g 2.02 g

fructose8.79 g 2.36 g

sorbitol0.17 g 0.05 g

glucose   8.08 g 2.16 g

lactose content0.00 g 0.00 g

20. Salad with watermelon

Melon salad from the category of raw food recipes + summer recipes

working time: 15 minutes.

Completed in: 15 minutes.

calories: 309

Level: Easy

ingredients For 2 people

- leaf lettuce 350 grams
- watermelon 175 grams
- Sunflower seeds 3 tablespoons / 25g
- sesame 3 tablespoons / 20g
- lime juice 2 tablespoons / 10g
- olive oil 3 tablespoons / 25g
- maple syrup 1 teaspoon / 5g
- pepper something / 1g
- salt something / 3g

Preparation

1. Wash salad, dry, and tear into small pieces. Cut the watermelon into small cubes.
2. Mix the lime juice, sunflower seeds, sesame, oil and the maple syrup and season with salt and pepper.
3. Mix the salad, melon, dress it and arrange it on a plate. Bon Appetit!

Nutritional information

per servingper 100g

Kilojoules (calories) 1294 (309)422 (101)

protein 8.23 g 2.68 g

carbohydrates 20.24 g 6.59 g

fat21.63 g7.05 g

fructose   9.56 g3.11 g

sorbitol   0.00 g0.00 g

glucose   9.60 g3.13 g

lactose content 0.00 g0.00 g

21. Vegan Broccoli raw food apple salad
Completely without Thermomix

working time: 25 min.

Completed in: 25 min.

calories: 196

Level: Easy

ingredients For 4 people

- Broccoli 500 grams

- Apple 150 grams

- Red pepper 1 piece / 155g

- Sunflower seeds 40 grams

- Olive oil (native) 30 grams

- Verjus (vinegar substitute) 2 tablespoons / 15g

- Sugar syrup 1 tablespoon / 12g

- Salt 1 teaspoon / 4g

- Pepper something / 1g

Preparation

1. Wash broccoli, apple and pepper, and core. Who has no Thermomix, cuts everything by hand in the smallest bite-sized pieces.
2. For dressing oil, mix Verjus (as a vinegar substitute for histamine intolerance), sugar beet syrup, mustard, salt, and pepper. Add sunflower seeds and pour over the vegan broccoli salad. Stir well and let steep for 15 minutes.

Nutritional information

per serving   per 100g

Kilojoules (calories)822 (196) 363 (87)

protein   8.05 g 3.55 g

carbohydrates 16.85 g 7.43 g

fat   10.60 g 4.67 g

fructose   9.28 g 4.09 g

sorbitol   0.66 g 0.29 g

glucose6.94 g 3.06 g

lactose content 0.00 g 0.00 g

22. Beetroot smoothie
Tastes great, raw food recipe for smoothie beginner

working time: 10 minutes

Completed in: 10 minutes

calories: 168

Level: Easy

ingredients For 3people

•Beetroot (fresh) 1 piece / 150g

- cucumber / 100 gram

- Spinach leaves (frozen) 40 grams

- Apple 1 piece / 130g

- Orange / 1 piece / 120g

- Almonds (natural) 20 grams

- linseed 15 grams

- walnuts 15 grams

- water 300 milliliters

Preparation

1. Peel and quarter the beetroot (preferably with gloves), and place it in the blender.
2. Wash cucumber and apple and cut into pieces. Depending on whether it is organic or not, it may also peel. Peel the orange with the knife (it's quicker than the pulp), halve and add to the blender with the almonds, walnuts, and flaxseed.
3. Blend everything for about 1 minute with the blender (which ideally should have, at least, 800 watts + 1.5 liters).
4. The red beet smoothie tastes mild and sweet despite the many healthy ingredients. That's what makes the beetroot. Unlike many healthy green smoothies, this smoothie is for beginners. The red beet smoothie is also ideal for green smoothie fans who need variety.

5. The amount is sufficient with the specified amount of water for three large glasses of about 0.3 liters and is quite viscous. The smoothie should, therefore, be served with a spoon. The amount of water can also be varied, for those who like it more fluid.

Nutritional information

per serving per 100g

Kilojoules (calories)705 (168) 238 (57)

protein 5.42 g   1.83 g

carbohydrates 15.46 g   5.21 g

fat   9.15 g   3.08 g

fructose8.53 g   2.87 g

sorbitol0.18 g   0.06 g

glucose6.39 g   2.15 g

lactose content   0.00 g   0.00 g

23. Green smoothie with corn salad and banana
With walnuts, flaxseed, sesame, and lemon

working time: 10 minutes

Completed in: 10 minutes

calories: 300

Level: Easy

ingredients For 2 people

- Lamb's lettuce 125 grams
- Banana / 1.5 pieces / 180g
- lemon juice 35 grams
- walnuts 25 grams
- Linseed (ground / gluten-free) 25 grams
- sesame 1 tablespoon / 8g
- Apple juice (nature cloudy) 150 grams
- water 250 grams

Preparation

1. Thoroughly wash lamb's lettuce and add to the blender with the banana, lemon juice, walnuts, sesame seeds, apple juice, and water.
2. Blend everything for about 1 minute with the blender (which should have, at least, 800 watts + 1.5 liters).
3. The amount is sufficient with the specified amount of water for two large glasses á 0.3 liter of green smoothie and is quite viscous. The green smoothie should, therefore, be served with a spoon. The

amount of water can also be varied, from those who like it more fluid. Who can tolerate little fructose, can reduce the proportion of apple juice.

Nutritional information

per serving   per 100g

Kilojoules (calories)1256 (300)   315 (75)

protein8.01 g   2.01 g

carbohydrates 29.63 g   7.43 g

fat 15.96 g   4.00 g

fructose 16.19 g   4.06 g

sorbitol0.42 g   0.11 g

glucose 13.41 g   3.36 g

lactose content   0.00 g   0.00 g

24. Green protein shake (without powder)
Vegan protein shake, Omega-3-rich, anti-inflammatory

working time: 15 minutes.

Completed in: 15 minutes.

calories: 374

Level: Easy

ingredients For 2 people

- grapefruit juice 100 milliliters
- Kale (fresh) 150 grams
- Apple 1 piece / 130g
- cucumber / 0.5 pieces / 220g
- Celery (fresh) 50 grams
- Hemp seed (peeled) 7 tablespoons / 70g
- Banana / 0.5 pieces / 50g
- Peppermint (fresh) 15 grams
- Linseed oil (native) 1 tablespoon / 8g
- ice cubes 4 pieces / 80g

Preparation

1. Cut grapefruit in half. Express juice. Alternatively, orange juice or coconut milk can be used.
2. Wash all ingredients thoroughly. Remove stalk, green, and seeds. Chop the cucumber, chop the apple, celery, and cabbage and place it in the blender.
3. Put peeled hemp seeds, banana, mint, linseed oil, and ice cubes in the blender as well. Set this to the highest level and mix thoroughly to a protein shake. The eggshake must be smooth and even, with no

visible pieces. If it is not, add some water or juice and mix again.

4. The specified ingredients of the protein shake make about 800 ml - so about four small or two large glasses (calculated as two portions). Each protein shake contains a whopping 16 grams of protein, all without protein powder.

5. This green protein shake without protein powder is ideal for those who like it naturally - WITHOUT protein powder - or for those who have no protein powder on hand. The protein shake is even vegan and without soy. In celeriac allergy, omit the celery stalks.

Nutritional information

  per serving   per 100g

Kilojoules (calories) 1567 (374)   359 (86)

protein 16.79g   3.85g

carbohydrates   28.07g   6.43g

fat 21.22g   4.86g

fructose   12.92g   2.96g

sorbitol 0.27g   0.06g

glucose 12.50g   2.86g

lactose content   0.00g   0.00g

25. Quinoa salad with carrots

Moroccan quinoa salad, gluten-free, vegan, healthy

working time: 35 minutes

Completed in: 35 minutes

calories: 504

Level: Easy

ingredients For 4 people

- quinoa 200 grams
- carrots 5 pieces / 300g
- Almonds (natural) 100 gram
- Organic lemon 1 piece / 60g
- Garlic cloves 1 piece / 3g
- Parsley (fresh) 20 grams
- Tahini from sesame 3 tablespoons / 25g
- Olive oil (native) 4 tablespoons / 32g
- raisins 50 grams

Preparation

1. Wash quinoa in a strainer under running water and cook in salted water for 20 minutes.

2. Wash carrots, peel and cut into thin strips or slices with a vegetable peeler.
3. Wash the parsley, shake it dry, pluck leaves from the stems, and chop. Chop almonds roughly. Wash the lemon, rub dry and rub off half of the peel. Halve lemon, squeeze juice. Peel garlic, finely chop.
4. Tahin, garlic, lemon peel, salt, pepper, and two tablespoons of lemon juice and stir with the. Stir olive oil.
5. Mix the quinoa, carrots, parsley, dressing, sultanas, and almonds and let them pass briefly. That's all. You're done

Nutritional information

per serving   per 100g

Kilojoules (calories) 2109 (504) 1068 (255)

protein   14.52g7.35g

carbohydrates   48.63g 24.63g

fat 27.54g13.94g

fructose   8.12g 4.11g

sorbitol 0.11g   0.06g

glucose 8.06g   4.08g

lactose content   0.00g   0.00g

26. Gluten-free millet and carrot buckwheat bread
fructose-free, gluten-free wheat-free, vegan, yes

working time: 25 min.

Completed in: 1 hour 40 minutes

calories: 85

Level: normal

ingredients For 30 people
- buckwheat 150 grams
- millet 200 grams
- carrots 200 grams
- Oatmeal (gluten-free) 125 grams
- water 550 grams
- salt 2 teaspoons / 10g
- Sunflower seeds 50 grams
- Linseed flour (gluten-free) 25 grams
- sesame 25 grams
- Flohsamenschalen 30 grams
- Weinstein baking powder (gluten-free) 1 pack / 17g
- olive oil 3 tablespoons / 25g

Preparation

1. Crush the carrots coarsely with a blender. If you do not have a blender, you can also rub the carrots.
2. Millet and buckwheat in a blender or flour mill to flour or buy as flour.
3. Mix all dry ingredients (millet buckwheat, gluten-free oat flakes, psyllium seed, salt, cumin, baking powder, and seeds).
4. Process with the carrots and water in a kneading machine or with your hands to make a buckwheat bread dough. Do not add all the water at once. Make sure that the bread dough is not too firm or too soft. Depending on how finely the millet and buckwheat flour is ground, a little more or less water is needed.
5. Lay out a box tin with baking paper, cover the ground with oatmeal and pour in the dough. Carve the millet and carrot buckwheat bread dough several times with a knife.
6. Preheat oven to 200 degrees. Then bake for 40 minutes at 200 degrees, tighten the incisions, and then bake for another 35 minutes at 180 degrees. Remove from the oven and let it cool completely, then cut. Ready is a delicious millet-carrot-buckwheat bread, which is nice juicy, thanks to the carrots.
7. From the buckwheat bread, you can cut 30 thin cuts. Good Appetite!

8. The gluten-free millet and carrot buckwheat bread lasts four days. You can also freeze it well in slices and toast later.

Nutritional information

per serving   per 100g

Kilojoules (calories)355 (85)   756 (181)

protein   2.62 g   5.59 g

carbohydrates12.09 g   25.78 g

fat 2.64 g   5.63 g

fructose   0.62 g   1.31 g

sorbitol   0.00 g   0.00 g

glucose   0.62 g   1.32 g

lactose content 0.00 g   0.00 g

27. Oven-baked vegetables

Delicious baked vegetables from the oven.

working time: 15 minutes.

Completed in: 45 min.

calories: 353

Level: Easy

ingredients For 2 people

- •Zucchini / s 2 pieces / 400g
- •Potato / 4 pieces / 360g
- •Cherry tomatoes 10 pieces / 100g
- •carrots 3 pieces / 200g
- •Thyme (fresh) something / 3g
- •Parsley (fresh) something / 5g
- •Rosemary (fresh) something / 3g
- •black pepper (freshly ground) something / 2g
- •salt something / 5g
- •Olive oil (native) 4 tablespoons / 30g

Preparation

1. Wash the vegetables. Wash, peel and chop the potatoes and carrots. Slice the zucchini. Then wash the herbs and finely cut. The cherry tomatoes stay whole.
2. Put the oven vegetables in a large casserole dish or on a clean baking tray, add the herbs, and mix well with the olive oil.
3. Cook the vegetables in a preheated oven at 180 degrees for 25-30 minutes. In between, stir, at least, once and add some water to the casserole dish if

necessary. After baking, season the baked vegetables with salt and pepper and serve.

Nutritional information

per serving   per 100g

Kilojoules (calories)1479 (353) 267 (64)

protein   9.12 g 1.65 g

carbohydrates   41.68 g 7.52 g

fat 15.98 g2.88 g

fructose7.19 g1.30 g

sorbitol0.00 g0.00 g

glucose 7.05 g1.27 g

lactose content   0.00 g 0.00 g

28. Beetroot salad with walnuts

vegan, clean food, healthy weight loss, omega-3-rich

working time: 15 minutes.

Completed in: 15 minutes.

calories: 501

Level: Easy

ingredients For 2 people

- Beetroot (fresh) 400 grams

- Red onions 1 piece / 50g

- walnuts 80 grams

- Thyme (fresh) something / 10g

- Linseed oil (native) 3 tablespoons / 25g

- Apple Cider Vinegar 1 tablespoon / 12g

- honey 1 teaspoon / 5g

- salt 0.5 teaspoon / 3g

- pepper something / 2g

Preparation

1. Roast walnuts in a pan.
2. Peel and dice beetroot. Wash thyme, dry, and pluck from the stems. Peel the onion and finely chop.
3. Add the remaining ingredients (linseed oil, apple cider vinegar, honey, salt, and pepper) to dressing and add to the walnut beetroot mix.
4. Stir onions, red beets, roasted walnuts, and the dressing, arrange on plates and decorate with thyme. Ready is the beetroot salad - without apple!

Nutritional information

per serving   per 100g

Kilojoules (calories)   2096 (501) 714 (171)

protein 10.00 g   3.41 g

carbohydrates 23.25 g   7.92 g

fat 41.10 g   14.00 g

fructose11.45 g   3.90 g

sorbitol 0.00 g   0.00 g

glucose 11.48 g   3.91 g

lactose content 0.00 g   0.00 g

29. Tahin dressing

Oriental sesame dressing for delicious salads

working time: 10 minutes

Completed in: 10 minutes

calories: 99

Level: Easy

ingredients For 3people

•orange juice 3 tablespoons / 25g

•lemon juice 1 tablespoon / 8g

•Tahini from sesame 3 tablespoons / 30g

•Olive oil (native) 1 tablespoon / 10g

•maple syrup 1 teaspoon / 6g

•salt something / 3g

•black pepper (freshly ground) something / 1g

Preparation

1. For the Tahin dressing, squeeze orange and lemon-fresh.
2. Measure out three tablespoons of orange juice and 1 liter of lemon juice and stir well with the Tahin, olive oil, maple syrup, salt, and pepper.
3. The Tahindressing goes very well with lettuce or broccoli salad and is enough for 3 to 4 servings.

Nutritional information

per serving per 100g

Kilojoules (calories)414 (99) 1495 (357)

protein   1.89 g6.83 g

carbohydrates 4.47 g16.14 g

fat   8.17 g29.54 g

fructose   0.47 g1.69 g

sorbitol   0.00 g0.00 g

glucose   1.84 g6.64 g

lactose content 0.00 g 0.00 g

30. Basic dressing for salads

The basic recipe for basic salads

working time: 10 minutes

Completed in: 10 minutes

calories: 216

Level: Easy

ingredients For 2 people

- lemon 1 piece / 80g
- Olive oil (native) 4 tablespoons / 45g
- Parsley (fresh) 2 tablespoons / 3g
- black pepper (freshly ground) something / 1g
- Seasoned Salt something / 3g

Preparation

1. Squeeze out the lemon, stir the lemon juice in a bowl, and add the olive oil.
2. Wash parsley or other herbs and chop finely.
3. Stir parsley and spices under the dressing - ready!
4. The basic dressing is suitable for every salad

Nutritional information

per serving per 100g

Kilojoules (calories)905 (216)   1371 (327)

protein 0.42 g0.63 g

carbohydrates1.73 g2.63 g

fat   22.76 g34.49 g

fructose0.79 g1.19 g

sorbitol0.00 g0.00 g

glucose0.85 g1.29 g

lactose content 0.00 g0.00 g

CHAPTER 8: MAIN MEAL RECIPES

VEGAN FITNESS KEBAB

Ingredients

- 1/2 packet Vegan Döner (brand "Wheaty")
- 75 g Parboiled Rice
- Two tomatoes
- 1.2 onions
- 150 g lettuce
- 150 g Soy yogurt (brand "Alpro")
- Something fresh herbs and spices
- Maybe something olive oil

Preparation

Preparation time: 20 minutes

1. Thoroughly wash the lettuce, tomatoes, and onion, and cut them into small pieces.
2. Meanwhile, cook the rice
3. Roast the vegan doner, it must be nice and crispy
4. Put the rice portion together with the salad, the tomatoes and the onions on a plate
5. Season the soy yogurt with fresh herbs and spices (maybe some olive oil) and pour over the salad

6. Finally, spread the fried vegan doner over it, and season with some kebab seasoning

Nutritional values per serving

Calories 680 kcal

Fat 19 g

Carbohydrates 78g

Protein 44 g

PUMPKIN PASTA: PENNE WITH CREAMY PUMPKIN SAUCE

Fall time is pumpkin time, so today, there is a delicious pumpkin noodle dish that is not only very simple but also prepared quickly.

You can find the pumpkin in almost every supermarket, but it is best to resort to regional and fresh produce from the farmers market. Pumpkins have season between August and December and peak in October. But they are almost always available next to the season.

Originally, the pumpkin comes from South America. In the early Middle Ages, it spread throughout Europe and is now grown throughout Austria.

Worth knowing is that all pumpkin varieties have to be peeled except for the Hokkaido pumpkin. Incidentally, pumpkins can also be eaten raw and are ideal for freezing. The pumpkin seeds are also delicious, especially in Styria, an essential part of the regional cuisine, as well as the delightful pumpkin oil. The pumpkin goes well with both savory and sweet foods.

The cooking time is 30 minutes

The portion is for two people

Ingredients

- 600 ml of water
- 200 g of floury potatoes
- 300 g Hokkaido pumpkin
- 1/2 tsp salt
- oregano
- paprika
- Knife tip turmeric
- 180 g penne or another type of pasta
- Pumpkin seed oil and cocktail tomatoes for garnish

Instructions

1. Peel the potatoes, cut into small cubes and cook with the also diced pumpkin (can be used with shell) in a pot with water and a little salt.
2. When pumpkin and potatoes are cooked, puree with ½ tsp salt, paprika, oregano, and turmeric in a

blender or with a hand blender until a cream is formed.
3. Now, the penne can be cooked in saltwater and lifted under the pumpkin cream.
4. If necessary, garnish with pumpkin seed oil and cocktail tomatoes.

MEDITERRANEAN QUINOA PAN WITH SHEEP'S CHEESE

This Mediterranean quinoa pan is made with plenty of vegetables and fresh herbs. Some sheep's cheese completes the taste and makes the dish complete!

Quinoa contains a lot of high-quality, vegetable protein, which is essential for the maintenance of the muscles, for example. Also, the so-called "grain of the Inca" contains many essential vitamins and minerals. Besides, quinoa is gluten-free - as it is not a real cereal! This is especially important for people who have celiac disease!

We prefer to refine this dish with fresh herbs such as rosemary, basil, and oregano. These herbs can even grow on the balcony quite uncomplicated, so you can always have fresh herbs at home for little money!

Sheep cheese contains around 17% very much protein. However, since it contains almost as much fat, it should, of course, only be enjoyed in moderation. To our vegetable quinoa pan, the cheese fits wonderfully and refines the dish with its spicy aroma.

Mediterranean quinoa pan with sheep's cheese

Cooking time   50 minutes

Two portions

Ingredients

- 1/2 cup of quinoa
- One spring onion
- Two cloves of garlic
- 200 g cocktail tomatoes
- a few olives inserted
- 1/2 zucchini
- 1/2 paprika
- 100 g sheep's cheese
- Fresh rosemary
- Oregano
- Basil
- Salt
- Pepper
- A little olive oil for searing

Instructions

1. First, cook the quinoa bite-proof according to the package instructions.
2. In the meantime, cut the vegetables and chop the garlic cloves.
3. Also, chop the herbs.
4. Fry the onion and garlic in a pan with a little oil.
5. Add the remaining vegetables and cook for about 5-10 minutes.
6. When the quinoa is ready, it is added to the vegetables and briefly topped with the herbs.
7. Serve the dish on a plate and garnish with the sheep's cheese!

GYOZA (DUMPLINGS) WITH SPICY CABBAGE SALAD

These Japanese dumplings (Gyoza) are first sautéed and then steamed - so not only an exceptional consistency but also pleasant roasted aromas – a simple recipe that can be served as a starter or light meal!

There are dozens of different types of preparation and fillings for these delicious dumplings. We have chosen this recipe for a mixture of vegetables and beef — Served Gyoza on spicy Asian slaw. For dipping, soy sauce, sesame oil, and rice vinegar are mixed to create an aromatic and tasty dish.

This recipe has an unusually high proportion of fresh vegetables, as the coleslaw is the base, and also the filling of Gyoza contains lots of vegetables. Among other things, the contained beef serves as a protein source, and the dough for the Gyoza includes filling carbohydrates.

This dish is perfect for hot summer days and garden parties!

Gyoza (dumplings) with spicy cabbage salad

cooking time   90 minutes

Four portions

Ingredients

- 300 g spelled flour
- 1/2 teaspoon salt
- 150 ml of water cook
- Some flour for dusting
- 300 g beef-clad
- Two spring onions
- Two cloves of garlic
- 150 g mushrooms (champignons, herb saplings,)
- One carrot
- 150 g of white cabbage
- One tablespoon soy sauce
    - EL Agavendicksaft
- 1/2 tablespoon sesame oil

- salt
- Pepper at will
- a little coconut oil for searing

Ingredients for the coleslaw

- 1/2 Krauthäuptel
- One carrot
- 1/2 paprika
- One spring onion
- 1/2 teaspoon chili powder
- 1/2 teaspoon paprika powder
- Two tablespoons of vinegar
- 1 TL Agavendicksaft
- One teaspoon soy sauce
- salt
- Pepper at will

Ingredients for the sauce for dipping

- Three tablespoons soy sauce
- 1.5 tablespoons of vinegar
- 1 EL Agavendicksaft
- A few drops of sesame oil

Instructions

1. First, prepare the dough: Mix the flour with ½ tsp salt, and then add the boiling water while stirring constantly.

2. Once the flour-water mixture is no longer too hot, the dough should be kneaded quickly smooth. To do this, dust the work surface with a little flour and knead the dough with your hands for about 5 minutes.

3. Cut the dough in half and shape into two rings. Cover the rings for 20 minutes.

4. In the meantime, the filling is prepared by finely chopping the onion and garlic. The mushrooms are cut into tiny pieces. The remaining vegetables are grated finely with a grater.

5. Mix the vegetables in a large bowl with the beef and the remaining ingredients — season with salt and pepper.

6. Now, the pieces of the same size are cut off, shaped into balls and rolled out with a rolling pin about 5 mm thick.

7. The round dough pieces are now filled with 1-2 tablespoons filling and closed by folding the edge.

8. Heat some coconut oil in a large pan with a lid and fry the Gyoza on one side until the bottom is golden brown. Then add 120 ml of water to the pan and cover with a lid. Steam the dumplings for 7-8 minutes.

9. For the coleslaw, finely chop or grate the cabbage and carrots. Cut the pepper into great strips. Mix the vegetables with the remaining ingredients and knead well to soften the herb — season with salt and pepper.

10. For the sauce for dipping, mix all the ingredients in a small bowl.
11. Arrange the Gyoza on the coleslaw and serve with the sauce.

PULLED JACKFRUIT WITH VEGETABLES FROM THE STEAMER

This fancy, vegetarian pulled jackfruit dish leaves nothing to be desired: fragrantly spiced Jackfruit, lots of fresh vegetables, and spicy tzatziki with lots of garlic! Also, we serve a combination of rice and red lentils - this provides an extra portion of protein and fiber.

The Jackfruit comes from tropical areas and is grown mainly in India, Thailand, Bangladesh, and Indonesia. Not so long ago, it has also made its way into European cuisine. It is a very versatile fruit that is often used as a meat substitute product. The reason for this is their texture: the fiber-rich pulp is reminiscent of slow-cooked meat such as " pulled pork " and can, therefore, be used for dishes such as chili, curry, burgers, and kebabs. The immature fruit is mostly used, which is stored and sold in cans or boxes in water. The Jackfruit is particularly suitable for cooking with the steamer, as the fruit fibers contained in the fruit are pleasantly soft, and the preparation improves the texture. We cook the Jackfruit together with aromatic spices and herbs, as well as with lots of fresh vegetables. By steaming, no oil is used, and you get a very low-fat dish!

The dish tastes best with a combination of rice and red lentils and spicy tzatziki for dipping. Even meat-eaters should not miss this pleasure and try the dish!

Pulled Jackfruit with vegetables from the steamer
The cooking time is 60 minutes

Two portions

Ingredients

Ingredients

- 280 g of Jackfruit (young Jackfruit in brine, drained off)
- One big onion
- Two cloves of garlic
- One pepper
- Four tomatoes
- 1/2 zucchini
- paprika
- chili powder
- salt
- pepper
- marjoram
- thyme
- Rosemary (dried, rubbed)
- 2/3 cup of rice
- 1/3 cup of red lentils

- Ingredients for the Tsatsiki
- One cucumber
- 200 g Greek yogurt (for the vegan alternative: soy yogurt unsweetened, natural)
- Three cloves of garlic
- salt
- pepper

Instructions

1. Slightly squeeze the Jackfruit with your fingers to create smaller, and fibrous pieces.
2. Cut the vegetables into medium-sized pieces and place them together with the Jackfruit in a perforated cooking dish.
3. Chop the garlic very finely and add it as well.
4. Season the mixture with the spices and herbs vigorously.
5. For the rice-lentil mixture, mix the legumes with the rice in an unperforated dish and add 1.5 cups of water and ½ teaspoon of salt.
6. Cook the rice-lentil mixture and the Jackfruit at 100 ° C for about 15-20 minutes in a steamer.
7. In the meantime, prepare the Tsatsiki: Halve the cucumber and remove the seeds. Then rub the cucumber halves roughly.
8. Press out the grated cucumber with your hands to remove some liquid.
9. Mix the cucumber with the Greek yogurt.

10. Finely chop garlic and mix into Tsatsiki. Season with salt and pepper.
11. Serve the pulled Jackfruit with vegetables together with Tsatsiki and the rice-lentil mixture!

QUINOA BOWL WITH MANGO SALAD AND FRESH VEGETABLES

Buddha bowl, Quinoabowl, feel-good bowl - everyone eats bowls right now! This is not a particular dish, but rather the way the meals are served - in a bowl. "Bowls" are exceptionally nicely prepared, colorful dishes with a large proportion of vegetables, wholegrain cereals, and legumes. We love this trend because it makes it easy to combine many delicious and healthy meals - which looks beautiful and is prepared very quickly!

The bowl in this recipe can, of course, be changed at will - get creative and use everything that you and your loved one can taste!

We use crispy fried pork, cooked quinoa, and lots of fresh vegetables in our recipe. Add a touch of exoticism to our dish of sweet and sour mango salad!

Our bowl contains many micronutrients from the vegetables and quinoa. It also contains healthy fatty acids due to the rapeseed oil used in the marinade. High-quality protein for our muscles and nervous system bring quinoa and pork!

Quinoa bowl with mango salad and fresh vegetables
The cooking time is 30 minutes

Two portions

Ingredients

- 250 g quinoa
- 250 g of pork cut into cubes
- One clove of garlic
- Two hands full of baby spinach fresh (or various salads)
- Three carrots
- 1/3 cucumber
- One pepper
- One mango (ripe)
- Some paprika powder smoked
- Some chili flakes
- salt
- Pepper to taste
- A little oil for searing
- 1/2 lemon juice
- Two tablespoons rapeseed oil
- Some coriander freshly chopped

Instructions

1. Cook the quinoa in salted water until crispy as per the package instructions.
2. Meanwhile, fry the sliced pork in a pan in a little oil and season with paprika, chili flakes, salt, and pepper.
3. Press and add the garlic. Stir well and fry until the meat is slightly crispy through and outside.
4. In the meantime, cut the vegetables (cucumber, pepper, carrot) and set aside.
5. For the mango salad, cut the mango into small pieces and mix with salt, pepper, fresh coriander, lemon juice, and rapeseed oil.
6. Serve in a bowl with cooked quinoa, roast pork, salad, and sliced vegetables and serve garnished with the mango salad.

KRAUTFLECKERL WITH FRESH HERBS AND SOUR CREAM DIP

These aromatic herbs are straightforward and quick to prepare. It also tastes great and is still healthy!

Are you looking for a dish that does not take much time in preparation and tastes right for the whole family? Then we have just the right thing for you! These herbs with herbs and sour cream dip are cooked in less than half an hour! We like to use spells dumplings, which contain more nutrients than wheat noodles and taste, at least, as good!

Although the herb is a typical winter vegetable, it also tastes good in summer! This recipe is, therefore, great to use up the last herb before summer.

The fresh herbs, which already grow on the balcony or in the garden in May, give the dish a particularly fresh and aromatic note - utterly different from the usual way of using cabbage!

We serve a refreshing sourcream dip with sour cream, spices, and chives for this dish! The creamy consistency and the fresh taste harmonize with the rest of the ingredients!

Krautfleckerl with fresh herbs and sour cream dip
The cooking time is 25 minutes

Two portions

Ingredients

Ingredients for cabbage with fresh herbs

- 280 g spelled dumplings
- One onion big
- 100 g bacon (for the vegetarian variant: smoked tofu)
- 300 g of white cabbage
    o TL agave syrup or honey
- salt
- pepper

- Nutmeg grated
- Some basil fresh
- A little parsley fresh
- Some chives fresh
- Two tablespoons rapeseed oil for searing

Ingredients for the sourcream dip

- 1/2 pack of sour cream
- 1/2 package of Creme Fraiche
- salt
- pepper
- Some chives fresh

Instructions

1. Cook the noodles in plenty of salted water according to the package instructions.
2. In the meantime, cut the onion and the bacon or tofu into beautiful cubes and sauté in the oil in a large pan.
3. Add the agave syrup or honey and caramelize briefly.
4. Rub the cabbage to produce skinny strips.
5. Add the herb to the pan and sauté until it is firm.
6. Strain the noodles and fry cold. Then add to the pan.
7. Finely chop the herbs and set aside.
8. Season the cabbage with the spices, and finally, add the chopped herbs.

9. For the dip, cut the chives into fine rings and mix with the remaining ingredients until a creamy consistency is obtained.
10. Serve the krautfleckerl with the dip, and some herbs sprinkled on it!

JACKFRUIT KEBAB WITH CASHEW GARLIC SAUCE

That a vegan kebab is so easy to prepare and can taste it's original confusingly similar, we would not have thought. The wonderful Jackfruit makes it possible.

Matching a Cashew garlic sauce, this sauce is slightly viscous. If you prefer a little more fluid, add some more water.

Jackfruit kebab with cashew garlic sauce
Cooking time   40 minutes

Three portions

Ingredients

Bread with filling:

- Three pita bread (gluten-free)
- 100 g of pickle salad
- One medium tomato
- One small cucumber
- 2 tbsp olive oil

- 1 tsp basil chopped
- Salt to taste
- Freshly ground pepper
- One portion of Jackfruit oriental spiced
- 3 EL frying oil

Sauce:

- 100 g of cashew nuts
- water
- One clove of garlic
- 2 EL Hefeflocken
- Salt to taste
- Freshly ground pepper

Instructions

Preparation filling:

1. Heat the pita bread according to the instructions on the package and then cut open halfway in the middle.
2. For the filling, wash the salad, tomato, and cucumber. Cut the tomato (without a green stalk) and the cucumber (with peel) into 1 to 2-centimeter pieces and mix. Add the olive oil, basil, and salt, and pepper to the tomato-cucumber mixture and mix well.
3. Fry the Jackfruit for about 10 minutes in a pan over medium heat in oil until crispy.

4. To finish, add one-third of the pickle salad to the sliced pita loaves, spread the tomato-cucumber mixture over the loaves, and add the fried Jackfruit. Drizzle the kebab with cashew garlic sauce - and the best vegan kebab in the world is ready!

Preparation sauce:

1. Put the cashew kernels in the high-performance blender with enough water to cover the kernels.
2. Peel the garlic clove, slice it and add the yeast flakes to the blender. Puree all ingredients to a creamy mixture. Taste the sauce with salt and pepper.

Spaghetti with vegan cheese sauce and broccoli lactose-free, gluten-free, free from soy and nuts

Spaghetti with vegan cheese sauce and broccoli lactose-free, gluten-free, free from soy and nuts

A vegan cheese sauce made from vegetables - can that taste good? Definitely yes! We have developed this recipe so that no one has to do without a creamy spaghetti sauce with a cheesy taste. The result can be seen! Try it; you will not regret it!

The base of the sauce consists of boiled carrots, potatoes, and peeled cannabis seeds. The taste reminiscent of cheese gets it through the used yeast flakes, some mustard, and lemon juice. Yeast flakes and hemp seeds can be found in well-stocked supermarkets or the health food store! The recipe is refined with a little parsley, garlic, and steamed broccoli.

Hemp seeds contain a lot of unsaturated fatty acids and high-quality, vegetable protein. You will be particularly creamy by the cooking and the subsequent pureeing and also give the sauce a slightly nutty taste.

Spaghetti with vegan cheese sauce and broccoli
lactose-free, gluten-free, free from soy and nuts

cooking time   50 minutes

Two portions

Ingredients

- 250 g spaghetti gluten-free (e.g., corn or rice flour)
- Two potatoes
- Two carrots
- 1/2 onion
- Two cloves of garlic
- Three tablespoons of hemp seed peeled
- 1/2 tsp hot mustard
- Four heaped tablespoons of yeast flakes
- Two tablespoons of lemon juice
- Two handfuls of broccoli florets
- salt

- Pepper to taste
- A little parsley fresh
- Some hemp seeds to sprinkle

Instructions

1. Peel potatoes, carrots, and onion and cut into medium-sized pieces. Boil the vegetables together with the hemp seeds in a pot in a little water until the vegetables are very soft.
2. Strain the vegetables and hemp seeds, collecting the water (still needed!).
3. Puree the cooked ingredients together with the garlic cloves, the yeast flakes, the lemon juice, and the mustard, gradually adding some cooking water until a creamy consistency is obtained. Then season with plenty of salt and pepper. Put the sauce in a saucepan and warm briefly.
4. Meanwhile, cook the noodles according to the package instructions and steam the broccoli in a little water until firm. Then strain both.
5. Finely chop the parsley.
6. Mix the pasta with the sauce, garnish with the broccoli and serve with some parsley, and some hemp seeds sprinkled!

TURKEY SLICED IN MUST MUSTARD SAUCE WITH WHOLEGRAIN RICE.

This sliced turkey is served in a must mustard sauce and refined with green peas, mushrooms, and crunchy paprika. It is a typical dish for the cold season and can be prepared with any vegetables.

The turkey is by frying with wine poured - this is then reduced so that only the flavors, not but alcohol remains. This gives this dish an exceptional taste. The must aroma is accompanied by spicy mustard - this underlines the fruity note and brings along the necessary spiciness.

Green peas are a real all-rounder in the kitchen - they provide high-quality protein and plenty of fiber. Anyone who buys them frozen can add them to all sorts of dishes and spice up the nutritional value of many dishes. They are therefore ideal in winter, where the regional selection of vegetables is not as big as in spring or summer.

For this dish, we prefer to serve brown rice: it has to cook a bit longer than husked rice but contains more fiber, vitamins, and minerals. It also causes blood sugar levels to rise more slowly and lasts longer! Therefore, this recipe is also particularly suitable for people with diabetes.

Cooking time   60 minutes

Two portions

Ingredients

- 1/2 cup of wholegrain rice
- One red onion
- 200 g of turkey meat
- 100 g mushrooms
- 200 ml of must
- 1 tsp mustard hot
- 1.5 tsp corn starch
- 200 ml of cream
- 150 ml vegetable broth
- One hand full of green peas TK
- One large red pepper
- salt
- Pepper to taste
- a little oil for searing

Instructions

1. Cook the rice according to the package instructions.
2 Chop the onion and fry in some oil in a pan.

3 Cut the turkey meat and mushrooms into mouth-sized pieces and sauté as well.

4 When the meat has turned slightly brown, add the must and let the liquid evaporate. Then add vegetable stock, cream, and peas and let boil briefly.

5 Cut the pepper into medium-sized pieces and add.

6 Mix the cornstarch with a little cold water until no lumps are visible and then add to the chopped meat. Stir well and simmer for about 5 minutes over low heat.

7 Add mustard, salt and pepper, and season to taste.

8 Serve the sliced meat with the rice.

FRIED NOODLES WITH DUCK BREAST STRIPS AND ASIAN GARLIC SAUCE

These Asian fried noodles with duck breast strips are quick to prepare and will delight your guests in any case!

We use whole wheat Mie noodles, which contain fiber and fill you up for a long time. Also, we use a lot of fresh vegetables, which is only seared briefly and so particularly crisp and rich in vitamins, remains.

The duck is sautéed twice, making it especially tasty and, above all, crispy. Together with the aromatic-spicy garlic sauce, it creates an authentic dish for an Asian evening!

The fried noodles are also perfect for precooking: prepare a more substantial amount and keep in the fridge for the rest of the week. So you can quickly warm up a portion if you do not have time to cook!

The dish also tastes good with chicken or beef strips and can also be prepared vegetarian with tofu pieces. You can also get creative with vegetables: shiitake mushrooms or bean sprouts are especially useful. It is best to use vegetables of the season - so only the freshest and most regional vegetables are served!

Fried noodles with duck breast strips and Asian garlic sauce

Cooking time   90 minutes

Two portions

Ingredients

Ingredients for the fried noodles with duck breast strips

- Two portions of wholegrain Mie noodles Southeast Asian wheat noodles
- Two duck breast fillets
- One small piece of ginger
- Two carrots
- Two spring onions
- One handful of broccoli florets
- One handful of Chinese cabbage cut
- Four large mushrooms
- salt
- pepper
- Chilli powder to taste
- Sesame to the sprinkling
- A little oil for searing

Ingredients for the garlic sauce

- 50 ml of soy sauce
- 100 ml of water
- One teaspoon sesame oil
- 1 tbsp rice vinegar or apple cider vinegar
- 1/2 orange juice (orange)
- 1tbsp brown sugar
- Four cloves of garlic
- One small piece of ginger
- Three tablespoons cornstarch
- salt
- pepper

Instructions

1 First, make the sauce: mix the liquid ingredients for the sauce in a pot and dissolve the sugar in it. Ginger and garlic very finely cut and also mix. Dissolve the cornstarch in a little water and add. Bring to a boil over low heat and then cook until a thick consistency is obtained. Finally, season with salt and pepper.

2 Then prepare the fried noodles: Cook the noodles bite-proof according to the package instructions.

3 Cut carrots, broccoli, and mushrooms into medium-sized pieces, and dice the ginger very finely.

4 Cut the spring onions into fine rings and fry together with the ginger in a non-stick pan in a little oil until translucent.

5 Add the sliced vegetables and Chinese cabbage and cook for about 10 minutes, stirring well.

6 Strain the pasta and fry for about 5 minutes on a high with the vegetables — season with salt, pepper, and chili powder.

7 For the duck breast strips, season the meat with salt and pepper, cut diamond-shaped on the skin side, and fry in some oil in a non-stick pan for approx. Seven minutes, then turn over and fry for another 5 minutes.

8 Remove the meat from the pan and cut it into strips. Then put it back into the pan and roast again on a high level for about 3 minutes until crispy. Finally, add about two tablespoons of the garlic sauce and pan well. Caramelize the duck briefly and then remove it from heat.

9 Serve the fried noodles together with the duck breast strips and garnish with a little garlic sauce and sesame.

RICE BOWL WITH BEEF AND SHORT ROASTED VEGETABLES

For our rice bowl, we combine crispy -fried beef together with spicy, briefly sautéed vegetables in a light sauce. You can use any vegetable that has just season and combine their favorite varieties! If you want, you can cook more rice, vegetables, and meat - that way you have a delicious dish in the fridge, if you do not have time to prepare.

We season the beef with some soy sauce and maple syrup. When sautéing the caramelized sugar in the maple syrup and the meat gets a slightly sweet note and a crunchy crust. The beef is in our recipe, the source of protein, because it contains valuable protein, which can be used by the body as well.

The vegetables are sautéed brief and then steamed in a sauce made of Worcester sauce and lime juice. This makes it particularly spicy, but remains crisp and gets through the lime juice a pleasantly fresh aroma.

If you want to cook a particularly healthy bowl, use brown rice as your carbohydrate base. It contains a lot of fiber, vitamins, and minerals because the shell has not been removed.

This dish contains a good portion of vegetables, complex carbohydrates, and high-quality protein - but most importantly, it tastes great!

Rice bowl with beef and short roasted vegetables
Cooking time   40 minutes

Four portions

Ingredients

- 1 cup of wholemeal rice or white rice (basmati rice goes very well with this recipe)
- 400 g of beef

- 1/3 leek/leek or two spring onions
- Four cloves of garlic
- One pepper
- 1/2 zucchini
- One hand full of broccoli florets
- 200 g mushrooms
- 1/2 lime juice or lemon juice
- 100 ml vegetable broth
- One teaspoon Worcester sauce
- One tablespoon soy sauce
- 1 EL maple syrup alternatively sugar or agave
- salt
- pepper
- Cumin
- paprika
- thyme
- chili flakes
- Sesame peanuts or spring onion rings to sprinkle
- A little oil for searing

Instructions

1. Cook the rice according to the package instructions.
2. In the meantime, prepare the vegetables: Cut the leeks into fine rings and two garlic cloves into small pieces — Fry both in a pan in a little oil.
3. Cut the peppers, zucchini, broccoli, and mushrooms into medium-sized pieces and fry in the pan. Then

add the vegetable stock and the lime juice and simmer for about 5 minutes.

4. Season with Worcester sauce, salt, pepper, cumin, paprika, thyme, and chili flakes as desired and set aside.

5. Cut the meat into small pieces and chop two garlic cloves into beautiful pieces. Fry both with a little oil in another pan. Season with soy sauce, maple syrup, and pepper. Fry the meat until it is inside, and the outside is nice and crispy.

6. Arrange some rice with the vegetable pan and meat in a bowl and sprinkle with sesame, chopped peanuts, or spring onion rings and serve.

MUSHROOM RAGOUT WITH PASTA AND CARAMELIZED TOFU

This mushroom ragout is a perfect feel-good dish for us: creamy ragout with noodles and crispy, slightly sweet tofu pieces. It is ideal for the fall and winter time - because it warms and gives a lot of energy!

Mushrooms are very versatile: they refine stir-fries, stews, can be baked or fried, and taste good with game dishes. This dish puts the mushrooms in the foreground, making them the star of this recipe. We use mushrooms, herb potherbs, and porcini mushrooms - but all edible mushrooms can be used - the more diversity, the better!

The tofu serves as a source of protein, and because it is extra crispy and slightly caramelized, it brings an exciting consistency to the dish! We like to use smoked tofu here. This is particularly spicy, and the smoke fits very well with the mushrooms.

The dairy products used in this recipe can easily be replaced with herbal alternatives - this is how to make a vegan dish.

Mushroom ragout with pasta and caramelized tofu
Cooking time   60 minutes

Four portions

Ingredients

- Four cloves of garlic
- 600g mushrooms (a mixture of mushrooms, porcini mushrooms, herb patties, etc.)
- 200 ml vegetable broth
- 100 ml of cream or 2 tbsp almond flour and 100waters
- 400 ml of milk (or a herbal alternative: nut milk, oat milk, etc.)
- Three tablespoons flour
- 300g of smoked tofu
- 1 tbsp sugar
- 600g of pasta
- parsley

- Chives fresh or frozen
- cumin
- Dried thyme
- some nutmeg
- One teaspoon soy sauce
- salt
- Pepper to taste
- a little oil for searing

Instructions

1. Cook the noodles bite-proof according to the package instructions.
2. Cut the leek into fine rings and fry in some oil in a saucepan.
3. Slice the mushrooms, add and fry for about 5 minutes.
4. Douse with vegetable stock and cook for about 15 minutes.
5. Add cream and milk, bring to a boil.
6. Smooth the flour with a little cold water and place in the ragout.
7. Stir well, season with soy sauce, chives, parsley, thyme, cumin, and nutmeg and simmer for another 15 minutes.
8. Meanwhile, cut the tofu into small cubes and sauté in a pan in about two tablespoons of oil — season well with salt and pepper.

9. When the tofu is golden brown, add the sugar and fry until the sugar is caramelized (Caution: lightly light)
10. Season the ragout with salt and pepper and serve with the pasta and tofu.

JACKFRUIT CHILI - A HEARTY, VEGETARIAN CHILI RECIPE

Everyone knows Chili con Carne! But have you ever tried chili with Jackfruit? This exotic fruit is also becoming more popular with us. This is mainly due to their consistency: the young, green Jackfruit reminiscent of the consistency of braised meat and is, therefore, a popular meat substitute. They make our vegetarian chili, especially tasty - not only vegetarians should try this recipe!

The Jackfruit is used in their immature form, especially in Asian cuisine, with India and Bangladesh are the main growing areas. The unripe fruits are peeled, and then cooked or pickled. The young, green Jackfruit can be found in our organic market, in Asian supermarkets, and occasionally in drugstores. Mostly, it is either shrink-wrapped or sold in cans. The fruits are meager in calories and consist mainly of fiber, thereby keeping a particularly long enough to regulate the blood sugar levels.

This chili contains valuable plant protein from beans and corn - a particularly beneficial combination where the bioavailability of the protein is higher than that of the individual ingredients. This means that the protein from beans and corn can be better utilized by the body than by both ingredients individually.

This dish is seasoned with chili flakes, oregano, cinnamon, cumin, garlic, and cilantro. Smoked paprika gives the dish a particularly intense, hearty note.

The dish tastes best with some cooked rice, whole-meal, or white bread, or just like that!

Jackfruit chili - a hearty, vegetarian chili recipe
The cooking time is 90 minutes

Four portions

Ingredients
- Two onions
- Four cloves of garlic
- 200 g of Jackfruit
- One can of corn
- One can of beans
- Two carrots
- One red pepper
- 100 ml of red wine
- 400 ml of tomato pieces or tomato sauce
- 200 ml vegetable broth
- 1 tsp sugar

- oregano
- cinnamon
- Ground coriander
- Cumin
- chili flakes
- Smoked paprika
- salt
- Pepper to taste
- a little oil for searing

Instructions

1. Dice the onions and fry in some oil in a large saucepan.
2. Press the garlic cloves and put them in the pot. Roast both glassy.
3. If necessary, chop and sauté the Jackfruit, stirring frequently.
4. Add the sugar and caramelize (Caution: Do not burn)!
5. Cut carrots and peppers into small pieces and add to the pot with corn and beans.
6. Deglaze with red wine and add the vegetable stock and tomato pieces, stir, and cook over medium heat for, at least, 30 minutes. Keep stirring.
7. Season the chili with the spices as you like and serve with rice or bread.

GLUTEN-FREE QUICHE WITH SEASONAL VEGETABLES

This recipe for a vegetable quiche is different from traditional quiche recipes: it is gluten-free! A large number of people need or want to abstain from gluten, which is why gluten-free alternatives are increasingly in demand.

Buckwheat flour and rice flour are used in this dish to make the dough. Buckwheat is not one of the usual cereals, but to the Knöterichgewächsen and is, therefore, free of gluten. It contains high-quality protein because it has all the essential amino acids. Besides, buckwheat is rich in minerals such as iron, magnesium, and zinc, as well as B vitamins. In the kitchen, it can be used in preparing cooked grains such as rice in vegetable pans, as a side dish, or as flour in different doughs.

The great thing about this recipe is that it can be prepared very variably. Various seasonal vegetables can be used to boil this delicious recipe. Find out more in our annual calendar for vegetables, which varieties are currently in season, and pick your favorite veggies - so seasonal and natural seasonal food can be!

Part 2

BREAKFAST RECIPES

1. Acid Reflux Free Blueberry Muffins

Servings = 12 >> Serving size =1 muffin

Cooking Time = 35 Minutes

4 TBSP LIGHT SPREAD

1 CUP SPLENDA, STEVIA, OR SWEETENER

2 LARGE EGGS

4 TBSP NON-FAT YOGURT

1 TSP PURE VANILLA EXTRACT

2 CUP ALL PURPOSE WHITE FLOUR

1 CUP WHOLE WHEAT FLOUR

4 TBSP WHEAT GERM

1/2 TSP SALT

2 TSP BAKING POWDER

1/2 TSP BAKING SODA

1 CUP NON-FAT BUTTERMILK

1 CUP BLUEBERRIES

Preheat oven to 350°F.

Split the egg yolk from the whites; whisk the whites until frothy. Mix together the light spread and egg yolk until smooth. Add in the Splenda or equivalent sweetener, yogurt, and vanilla. Sift the flour, germ, salt, baking powder, and baking soda into a mixing bowl and slowly bring together the dry and wet mixes. As you blend all together, add the buttermilk until nice and smooth. Fold the frothy egg whites into the mix, as well as the blueberries. Line muffin tins with muffin paper and place equal amounts into each; not overfilling beyond the paper liner. Bake for 15 – 20 minutes.

2. Acid Reflux Free Oatmeal

Servings = 2 >> Serving size =about 1 cup

Cooking Time = 15 Minutes

1 CUP QUICK OATS

1 CUP WATER

1 CUP 2% MILK

1/8 TSP SALT

3 TSP LIGHT BROWN SUGAR

2 TSP LIGHT SPREAD

Put a frying pan over the stove at medium to high heat. Add in oatmeal; cook for 5 minutes while stirring. The oatmeal should cook until golden brown; you're trying to toast the oats. Add water and let come to a boil, then reduce heat and add the rest of the ingredients. Cook for another 5 minutes stirring frequently.

3. Acid Reflux Free Scrambled Eggs

Servings = 4 >> Serving size =2 eggs

Cooking Time = 30 Minutes

6 LARGE EGG WHITES

2 LARGE EGG YOLK

4 TBSP WATER

1/4 TSP SALT

2 TSP UNSALTED BUTTER

16 OZ FRESH CRIMINI MUSHROOMS

1 PINCH FRESH GROUND BLACK PEPPER

Whisk the eggs up really well to ensure yolk and whites are mixed. Combine in water and salt, and whisk again until frothy. Melt butter in non-stick frying pan over medium heat. Saute mushrooms until golden brown ensuring to toss as to not allow any burning. Add frothy eggs into mushrooms and cook until fluffy. Add pepper to taste.

4. Acid Reflux Free Melon Smoothie

Servings = 2 >> Serving size =about 1 1/2 cups

Time = 18 Minutes

1 CUP NON-FAT YOGURT

12 OZ CANTALOUPE

1BANANA

2/3 CUP MANGO OR PAPAYA JUICE

Put all ingredients in a blender, or container with hand blender, and blend together thoroughly.

5. Acid Reflux Free Banana Bread

Servings = 16 >> Serving size =1 slice

Cooking Time = 80 Minutes

2 LARGE EGG YOLK

2 TBSP LIGHT SPREAD

1 1/3 CUP SPLENDA OR STEVIA

1 TSP PURE VANILLA EXTRACT

4 MEDIUM BANANAS

6 LARGE EGG WHITES

2 1/2 CUP ALL PURPOSE WHITE FLOUR

1 1/2 CUP WHOLE WHEAT FLOUR

1/2 TSP SALT

4 TSP BAKING POWDER

1 TSP BAKING SODA

1 TSP GROUND CINNAMON

1/2 TSP GROUND NUTMEG

1/2 CUP WHEAT GERM

1 CUP PECANS

1/2 CUP NON-FAT BUTTERMILK

4 TSP LIGHT BROWN SUGAR

Turn your oven to 325°F and line a loaf pan with non-stick aluminum foil; or use a non-stick loaf pan. Whisk the egg yolks together, then add the spread. Mash the bananas into the mix and at the same time add in the Splenda or sweetener, and vanilla. Take a second bowl and whisk egg whites until frothy. Then sift in the flour, salt, baking powder, baking soda, germ, and all spices into the egg yolk mix. Fold together the mix while adding pecans. Add the egg whites after all has been mixed in well. Lastly add the buttermilk, then pour into loaf pan. Bake until done; between 45-60 minutes.

6. Acid Reflux Free Lemon Muffins
Servings = 12 >> Serving size =1 muffin

Cooking Time = 30 Minutes

2 LARGE EGGs

2 TBSP LIGHT SPREAD

1 CUP SPLENDA OR STEVIA

4 TBSP NON-FAT YOGURT

1 TSP PURE VANILLA EXTRACT

4 TBSP POPPY SEEDS

2 TBSP LEMON ZEST

1/2 CUP FRESH LEMON JUICE

2 CUPs ALL PURPOSE WHITE FLOUR

1 CUP WHOLE WHEAT FLOUR

4 TBSP WHEAT GERM

1/2 TSP SALT

2 TSP BAKING POWDER

1/2 TSP BAKING SODA

2/3 CUP NON-FAT BUTTERMILK

Preheat the oven to 350°F and split the egg into yolk and whites. Put the yolks into a mixing bowl and add in the spread. Whisk in the Splenda, yogurt, vanilla, and poppy seed. Add the zest and lemon juice. Mix the dry ingredients together well, then combine wet and dry. Once blended together, add in the buttermilk and blend more. Whisk the egg whites until frothy then fold into the batter mix. Line a muffin baking tin with muffin paper and scoop batter into each not overflowing beyond the paper liner. Baking will take about 20 minutes.

7. Acid Reflux Free French Toast
Servings = 4 >> Serving size =2 slices toast

Cooking Time = 30 Minutes

6 OZ EGG SUBSTITUTE

4 TSP GRAND MARNIER ORANGE LIQUEUR

2 TBSP SPLENDA OR STEVIA

2 TBSP 2% MILK

1/2 TSP PURE VANILLA EXTRACT

1/2 CUP ORANGE JUICE

1/2 TSP GRATED ORANGE PEEL

8 SLICES SOURDOUGH BREAD

4 TSP LIGHT SPREAD

4 TBSP HONEY

1 TSP GRAND MARNIER

Mix together the egg, orange liqueur, Splenda, milk, vanilla, orange juice and zest. Heat up a non-stick frying pan over medium heat. Dunk the bread into the mixture until completely covered. Pan sear each piece until golden brown; reduce heat if needed as to not burn anything. Top with spread and honey.

8. Acid Reflux Free Granola

Servings = 12 >> Serving size =about 1 cup

Cooking Time = 60 Minutes

6 QUARTS WATER

2 2/3 CUPS STEEL CUT OATS

1 1/3 CUP QUINOA

1/2 CUP SLICED ALMONDS

1/2 CUP CHOPPED WALNUTS

1 CUP UNSWEETENED APPLESAUCE

1 TSP GROUND CINNAMON

1 TSP GROUND NUTMEG

1/4 TSP SALT

4 TBSP PURE MAPLE SYRUP

1/2 CUP RAISINS

1/2 CUP DRIED CRANBERRIES

Preheat your oven to 300°F and put the water in a large pan over high heat. When boiling, add the quinoa and oats, then reduce the heat and simmer for about 15 minutes. Once done, drain and put mix into a large bowl; mix together the nuts, spices, syrup, raisins and cranberries. Mix together well then spread over a baking sheet. Bake in over for about 45 minutes or until golden brown.

9. Acid Reflux Free Blueberry Cornmeal Pancakes
Servings = 4 >> Serving size =2 pancakes

Cooking Time = 30 Minutes

1 CUP BLUE CORNMEAL

1/2 CUP WHOLE WHEAT FLOUR

4 TSP SPLENDA OR STEVIA

2 TSP BAKING POWDER

1/2 TSP SALT

1 1/3 CUP NON-FAT BUTTERMILK

1/2 CUP EGG SUBSTITUTE

2 TSP PURE VANILLA EXTRACT

4 TBSP FRESH BLUEBERRIES

4 TSP LIGHT SPREAD

2 TBSP PURE MAPLE SYRUP

Put the dry ingredients into one bowl, and mix completely. Add in the buttermilk, vanilla, egg substitute, and whisk. Over medium to high heat place a non-stick frying pan. Dollop batter into frying pan, and sprinkle blueberries on top of each one. Cook for about 2 minutes then flip each pancake cooking for another minute or until golden brown.

10. Acid Reflux Free Strawberry Smoothie

Servings = >> Serving size =about 1 1/2 cups

Time = 18 Minutes

1/4 CUP NON-FAT YOGURT

1 CUP FRESH STRAWBERRIES

1/2 CUP MANGO JUICE

1/2 BANANA

Put all ingredients in a blender, or container with hand blender, and blend together thoroughly.

SOUP RECIPES

1. Acid Reflux Free Beef Stew

Servings = 12 >> Serving size =2 1/2 cups

Cooking Time = 90 Minutes

8 CUPS WATER

50 PEARL ONIONS (PEELED)

2/3 CUP ALL PURPOSE WHITE FLOUR

2 TSP SALT

1/2 TSP FRESH GROUND BLACK PEPPER

3 LBS FLANK STEAK (3/4 INCH CUBES)

COOKING SPRAY

1 LB BUTTON MUSHROOMS (QUARTERED)

2 CUP WHITE ONION (SLICED)

2 TBSP FRESH LEMON JUICE

2 TBSP WORCESTERSHIRE SAUCE

2 LB CARROTS (PEELED AND SLICED 1/4 INCH THICK)

4 BAY LEAVES

3 LBS RED POTATOES (PEELED AND 3/4 INCH CUBES)

1/4 TSP GROUND ALLSPICE

Over high heat, get some water just about to boil, then add onions and let cook for about 10 minutes. Drain water and put onions into a large pot. Mix together flour, salt and pepper and toss in cubes of steak ensuring to coat them well. Spray a skillet with cooking spray and over high heat, brown the steak cubes. Move the steak into the large pot of onions, add in lemon juice, and Worcestershire. Add carrots, bay leaves, potatoes, allspice and water to the pot and place in the oven, covered at 400°F. Cook for one hour stirring gently every fifteen minutes.

2. Acid Reflux Free Butternut Squash Soup

Servings = 8 >> Serving size =about 1 1/2 cups

Cooking Time = 60 Minutes

4 CUPS WATER

4 LBS BUTTERNUT SQUASH

1 TSP SALT

FRESH GROUND BLACK PEPPER

1 TSP DRIED THYME LEAVES

1/4 TSP GROUND NUTMEG

2 CUPS WATER

Put a large pan of water with a steamer basket over high heat and place cubed squash in the basket. Steam for about 30 minutes. Let cool, then add to water in the large pan and puree with a blender. Put this over low heat and add salt, pepper, thyme, and nutmeg. Stir in remaining water until consistency of a smoothie.

3. Acid Reflux Free White Bean & Kale Soup
Servings = 8 >> Serving size =about 2 cups as an entree, 1 cup as a starter

Cooking Time = 60 Minutes

4 TSP OLIVE OIL

24 OZ KALE

2 OZ PANCETTA OR LEAN HAM (DICED)

2 LARGE ONION (DICED)

4 LARGE CARROTS (PEELED AND DICED)

4 15 OZ CAN NO SALT ADDED WHITE BEANS (DRAINED AND RINSED)

8 CUPS WATER

2 TSP DRIED MARJORAM

1 TSP SALT

2 TSP FRESH GROUND BLACK PEPPER (TO TASTE)

2 TSP MAPLE SYRUP

Cut the kale into thin strips (almost like the size of noodles). Take two tsp of olive oil in a skillet over medium heat. Add kale & stir often for 5 minutes, then remove. Add the rest of the oil and diced pancetta and cook for 3 minutes. Add the rest of the ingredients and bring down to a simmer. Once carrots are tender, take half of the mix and blend until pureed; then mix back together. Heat until ready to serve.

4. Acid Reflux Free Tomato & Corn Soup

Servings = 8 >> Serving size =about two cups

Cooking Time = 120 Minutes

6 LBS TOMATOES

SPRAY OLIVE OIL

2 TSP OLIVE OIL

4 FRESH CORN COBS

1/2 CUPS WHITE ONION (DICED)

4 CLOVES GARLLC (MINCED)

4 CUPS LOW SODIUM CHICKEN OR VEGETABLE BROTH

4 CUPS WATER

1 CUPS WHITE WINE

2 TBSP FRESH ROSEMARY

2 TBSP FRESH THYME

1/2 TSP RED PEPPER FLAKES

Get your oven to 400°F then put tomatoes in a roasting pan; spray a little cooking oil over the tomatoes; roast for 1 hour. Place corn in a large pan, cover with water and cook for about 10 minutes until colors brighten. Cut kernels from the cob. Heat oil in a large pot over medium; brown onions. Add corn kernels, garlic; cook for about 2-3 minutes then remove from heat. Place roasted tomatoes in blender and puree then add to pot. Add rest of the ingredients and heat for 15-20 minutes. Serve.

5. Acid Reflux Free Chicken Soup

Servings = 8 >> Serving size =about 2 cups

Cooking Time = 60 Minutes

2 TSP OLIVE OIL

2 LARGE ONION (DICED)

4 RIBS CELERY (DICED)

4 LARGE CARROTS (DICED)

6 CORN COB (CUT KERNELS OFF COB)

2 LB BONELESS SKINLESS CHICKEN THIGHS (CUBED)

4 TSP GROUND CUMIN

2 TSP PAPRIKA

2 TSP CHILI POWDER

10 CUPS WATER

1 TSP SALT

FRESH GROUND BLACK PEPPER (TO TASTE)

TORTILLA CHIPS

Get oil heated in a large pot, add onion and cook for 5 minutes. Add celery, carrots, corn and chicken; cook for about 5 more minutes. Add the rest of the ingredients and simmer for about 45 minutes to 1 hour. Place the olive oil in a medium stock pot over medium high heat. Add the onion and cook, stirring frequently, for about 3 minutes. Serve topped with crumbled tortilla chips.

SALAD RECIPES

1. Chicken Salad

Servings = 8 >> Serving size =about 1 1/2 cups

Cooking Time = 45 Minutes

8 CUPS WATER

1 CUP WHITE WINE

2 LB BONELESS SKINLESS CHICKEN BREAST

8 RIBS CELERY (DICED)

4 CLOVES GARLIC (MINCED)

8 TBSP REDUCED-FAT MAYONNAISE

1/2 TSP SALT

FRESH GROUND BLACK PEPPER (TO TASTE)

Bring the water and wine to a boil in a large skillet. Reduce to a small bubble then add the chicken; poach for about 15 minutes. Make sure the inside of the chicken reaches 160°F. Cut into cubes and store in refrigerator in a large bowl. Once cool, add the rest of the ingredients. When ready to serve, place over leafy greens, or your favorite salad mix. Garlic may be left out if this is a GERD trigger for you.

2. Poppy Seed Salad

Servings = 12 >> Serving size =about 1/4 cup

Cooking Time = 30 Minutes

6 CUPS PAPAYA CHUNKS

1 CUP NON-FAT YOGURT

1 CUP REDUCED-FAT SOUR CREAM

2 CUP PAPAYA JUICE

2 TSP SALT

8 TBSP CILANTRO LEAVES

8 TBSP POPPYSEEDS

Put all ingredients in a blender and blend until smooth. Serve over leafy greens or your favorite salad mix.

3. Scallop Pasta Salad

Servings = 4-5 >> Serving size =about 2 1/2 cups

Cooking Time = 30 Minutes

SPRAY OLIVE OIL

16 OZ CRIMINI MUSHROOMS (SLICED)

6 QUARTS WATER

8 OZ WHOLE WHEAT OR GLUTEN FREE PENNE PASTA

8 TSP OLIVE OIL

2 TSP DRIED ROSEMARY (OR 1 TBSP. FRESH)

2 MEDIUM ZUCCHINI (CUT INTO LARGE DICE)

4 RIBS CELERY (DICED)

16 GREEN OLIVES (COARSELY CHOPPED)

1/2 TSP SALT

FRESH GROUND BLACK PEPPER (TO TASTE)

16 OZ SEA SCALLOPS

In a large skillet over medium high heat spray a little cooking oil and fry up mushrooms until browned. In another pot at the same time boil the penne until al dente. Once cooked add to large mixing bowl and add 6 teaspoons of olive oil; store in refrigerator. When mushrooms are browned, add to pasta. In the same skillet as your cooked the mushrooms, add more olive oil, reduce to medium heat and add rosemary and zucchini, and cook for about 5 minutes then add to the pasta. Add the rest of the ingredients except for the scallops and mix well. Once ready to serve, sear the scallops in a light spray of oil for 5 minutes each side; add to salad and serve.

4. The Waldorf Salad

Servings = 10-12 >> Serving size =3/4 cup

Cooking Time = 30 Minutes

4 MEDIUM GRANNY SMITH APPLES (CORED AND CUT INTO 1/4 INCH CUBES)

2 MEDIUM RED DELICIOUS APPLE (CORED AND CUT INTO 1/4 INCH CUBES)

2 TBSP FRESH LEMON JUICE

2 CUP CELERY (CUT INTO LARGE DICE)

1/2 CUP WALNUTS (COARSELY CHOPPED)

1/2 CUP RAISINS

1/2 CUP LOW-FAT MAYONNAISE

1/2 CUP LOW-FAT SOUR CREAM

3 TSP HONEY

Once you have cubes the apples, add lemon juice, to this add celery, walnuts, and raisins; toss well together. Add mayonnaise, sour cream, and honey and blend together. When ready to serve, serve with leafy greens, or your favorite salad mix.

5. Parmesan Salad

Servings = 6-8 >> Serving size =2 tablespoons dressing and salad

Cooking Time = 30 Minutes

4 TBSP REDUCED-FAT MAYONNAISE

4 TBSP NON-FAT BUTTERMILK

1/2 CUP 2% MILK

1 OZ PARMIGIANO-REGGIANO

1 TSP BALSAMIC VINEGAR

2 CUPS MIXED GREENS (LETTUCE, SPINACH, MACHE) (PER SERVING)

2 TBSP YELLOW BELL PEPPER (DICED PER SERVING)

2 TBSP CARROT (DICED PER SERVING)

1 TBSP RED BELL PEPPER (DICED PER SERVING)

1 OZ SWISS CHEESE (DICED PER SERVING)

1 OZ TURKEY BREAST (PER SERVING)

1 OZ HAM (PER SERVING)

In a blender, add mayonnaise, buttermilk, milk, add parmesan and blend until smooth. Pour over leafy greens, turkey, and ham. Top with peppers.

MAIN RECIPES

1. Kung Pao Beef

Servings = 4 >> Serving size =4 OZ beef with vegetables and rice

Cooking Time = 30 Minutes

16 OZ FLANK STEAK (CUBED)

2 TSP LOW-SODIUM SOY SAUCE

2 TSP SAKE OR SWEET WHITE WINE

1 TSP SESAME OIL

2 TSP RICE VINEGAR

2 TSP HONEY

1 TSP CORNSTARCH

2 CUPS WATER

1 CUP JASMINE RICE

1 TBSP SESAME OIL

1 INCH GINGER ROOT (MINCED)

2 TBSP RICE VINEGAR

2 TBSP LOW-SODIUM SOY SAUCE

3/4 CUP WATER

1/4 CUP DRY ROASTED PEANUTS (CHOPPED)

Take the soy sauce, sake, sesame oil, vinegar, honey, and cornstarch and blend in a large bowl. Coat the steak cubes in this mix then chill in the refrigerator. In a large pan, heat the water and stir in rice. Let simmer for about a half an hour. Add sesame oil and ginger and cook for another minutes. Add beef and cook until browned. Add the vinegar and soy sauce mix; serve over the rice and top with the peanuts.

2. GERD Free Meatloaf

Servings = 6 >> Serving size =1 slice

Cooking Time = 60 Minutes

1 LB LEAN GROUND BEEF

4 OZ FRESH BREAD CRUMBS

1 TSP DRIED OREGANO

1 TSP DRIED BASIL

1 TSP DRIED ROSEMARY

1 TSP DRIED THYME

1/2 TSP SALT

1/8 TSP GROUND BLACK PEPPER

3/4 CUP TOMATO SAUCE

Before starting, heat your oven to 325°F then line a meatloaf pan with foil. Mix beef, bread crumbs, spices, salt and pepper together in a large mixing bowl. Form into a loaf shape and place into pan. Press into pan until quite firm and there are no spaces. Cook for about a half an hour then top with tomato sauce; cook for another 25 minutes, or until internal temperature of 150°F. Remove and let stand for 10 minutes before serving.

3. Lamb Leg

Servings = 8 >> Serving size =4 OZ lamb with sauce

Cooking Time = 120 Minutes

2 LB BONELESS LEG OF LAMB

3 TBSP FRESH OREGANO

1/2 TSP SALT

FRESH GROUND BLACK PEPPER

1 TSP OLIVE OIL

1/2 CUP LOW SODIUM CHICKEN BROTH

1 TBSP UNSALTED BUTTER

Heat your oven to 325°F then start cutting off the extra fat and skin from the lamb leg. Inside the leg, rub in oregano and half of the salt. In a large skillet, heat up some olive oil on high; when hot enough add the lamb and sear until browned on each side. Once done, place in the oven and roast for about 45 minutes; ensuring to turn every 10 or 15. When the lamb reaches an internal temperature of 145°F it's done, and rest for about 15 minutes before slicing up. Using the same skillet without washing away the great lamb flavoring, heat up the chicken broth over high heat. Add the add the rest of the ingredients and reduce to about half; serve over the sliced lamb.

4. Philly Cheese Steak

Servings = 1 >> Serving size =1 sandwich

Cooking Time = 30 Minutes

OLIVE OIL SPRAY

1/2 MEDIUM ONION

1 MINI BAGUETTE (2.5 OZ OR LESS)

1 TBSP NON-FAT MAYONNAISE

2 OZ ROASTED FLANK STEAK OR LONDON BROIL

1/2 OZ REDUCED-FAT SWISS CHEESE

Heat a non-stick pan sprayed with olive oil over high heat. Add onions once hot and reduce to medium heat. Fry until browned. Set to broil on your oven and cu the baguette lengthwise like a sub; heat under the broiler until golden brown, remove and spread the mayo on each side. Slice the steak and quickly fry until cooked and place on top of the baguette. Put onion and cheese on top and broil in the oven again until cheese has melted. Serve hot.

5. Carbonara Pasta

Servings = 4 >> Serving size =2 OZ pasta with sauce and peas

Cooking Time = 30 Minutes

4 QUARTS WATER

8 OZ WHOLE WHEAT OR GLUTEN-FREE LINGUINE

4 TSP OLIVE OIL

4 CLOVES GARLIC (LIGHTLY CRUSHED)

4 OZ PROSCIUTTO (DICED)

2 CUP FROZEN PEAS (THAWED)

1/2 CUP WHITE WINE

4 LARGE EGGS

2 OZ PARMIGIANO-REGGIANO (GRATED)

FRESH GROUND BLACK PEPPER (TO TASTE)

Boil some water over high heat in a large sauce pan, then add pasta. In another pan heat up some olive oil and fry up the garlic and prosciutto. Reduce heat once it begins to brown up; add peas and reduce further to low heat. In a mixing bowl, whisk eggs and parmesan. When pasta has been cooked, add wine to the skillet, then the pasta. Pour pasta and wine then into the mixing bowl with egg and cheese once hot. Mix together well then serve hot.

6. Spaghetti & Meatballs

Servings = 2 >> Serving size =4 meatballs with 2 OZ pasta and 1/2 OZ cheese

Cooking Time = 30 Minutes

4 QUARTS WATER

2 OZ PER SERVING SPAGHETTI NOODLES

4 PER SERVING MEATBALLS

1/2 CUPS PER SERVING TOMATO SAUCE

1 OZ PARMIGIANO-REGGIANO

Over high heat, boil some water then add pasta. While the pasta is bubbling, put meatballs and sauce in a sauce pan and heat over medium. Once sauce gets hot enough, reduce heat to a simmer. Remove pasta from water, then move into sauce pan. Toss and serve with grated parmigiano.

7. Chicken Fajitas

Servings = 8 >> Serving size =one fajita

Cooking Time = 30 Minutes

2 MEDIUM WHITE ONION (PEELED AND SLICED)

2 RED BELL PEPPER

SPRAY OLIVE OIL

24 OZ BONELESS SKINLESS CHICKEN BREAST

1/2 TSP SALT

1/2 TSP GROUND CUMIN

1/2 CUP WATER

8 LOW-FAT SOFT FLOUR TORTILLAS

2 TSP NON-FAT SOUR CREAM (PER SERVING)

2 TBSP FRESH CILANTRO LEAVES (PER SERVING)

8 QUARTS WATER

4 OZ PER SERVING SPAGHETTI NOODLES

8 PER SERVING MEATBALLS

½ CUP PER SERVING TOMATO SAUCE

1 OZ PARMIGIANO-REGGIANO

Slice onion and place in large mixing bowl. Heat your oven to 350°F and roast red pepper for a half an hour, or until skin is bubbly and charred; ensure to turn peppers every so often to roast evenly. Once done, put into a paper bag and allow to cool. Once the peppers cool down, the skin will easily peel off. Remove seeds and slice into thin strips. Heat up a pan and fry up onions in a light coating of olive oil. Fry until browned, but ensure they do not burn. Add pepper slices when onions are ready, as well as the chicken, salt, and spices. Cook until chicken is browned. In a second pan over high heat, place one tortilla at a time and heat on either side for about 15 seconds each side. Once done, add chicken mixture, and remaining ingredients to each fajita.

8. Stuffed Turkey

Servings = 12 >> Serving size =about 5 OZ turkey with rice

Cooking Time = 90 Minutes

1 3/4 CUP WATER

1/2 CUP WILD RICE

1 CUP JASMINE OR BASMATI RICE

1/2 TSP SALT

1 TSP GRAPESEED OIL

1 LARGE SHALLOT (MINCED)

2 LARGE CARROTS (DICED)

1/4 CUP PISTACHIO NUTS (SHELLED)

1/4 CUP DRIED CURRANTS

1/2 TSP SALT

1/4 TSP FRESH GROUND BLACK PEPPER

1/2 TSP DRIED BASIL

1/2 TSP DRIED OREGANO

1 TSP DRIED ROSEMARY

1 BONELESS TURKEY BREAST WITH SKIN ON

8 SIX INCH DISPOSABLE SMALL WOODEN SKEWERS

In a large frying pan, heat water up to a boil then add rice and salt then reduce heat to a simmer. Cook covered until rice is done. While rice is in the middle of cooking, put oil in a medium sized skillet over medium heat and fry carrots and shallots for about 5 minutes; then add pistachios and fry for another 3-4 minutes. Add into the rice once done. To this mixture add currants, and all spices; toss together until blended well. Heat your oven to 350°F while butter flying the turkey open. Fill the opening with the rice mix and roll the breast fillet towards the butterfly skin portion. Use the skewers to hold the roll together. Put into a roasting pan and roast for about an hour and a half. Internal temperature should be over 155°F. Let stand once done for about 10 minutes.

9. Turkey Burgers

Servings = 4 >> Serving size =1 burger

Cooking Time = 30 Minutes

16 OZ GROUND TURKEY (BREAST IS BETTER)

1/2 TSP SALT

FRESH GROUND BLACK PEPPER

2 TSP EXTRA VIRGIN OLIVE OIL

1/2 TSP DRIED THYME LEAVES

4, 3/4 OZ SLICES REDUCED FAT SWISS CHEESE

4 WHOLE WHEAT OR GLUTEN-FREE HAMBURGER BUNS

1 TBSP NON-FAT MAYONNAISE (PER SERVING)

LETTUCE

TOMATO SLICES

Get a skillet hot in the oven at 375°F and combine turkey, salt & pepper, olive oil, and spice. Form equal sized burgers from the mix. When your skillet it hot enough, place burgers in skillet in the oven and cook for about 5 minutes on each side. Top with cheese and let melt (about 1 minute more of cooking time). Serve hot on a bun.

10. Seared Mustard Whitefish

Servings = 4 >> Serving size =4 OZ fish

Cooking Time = 30 Minutes

2 LARGE EGGS

6 TSP OLIVE OIL

4 TSP DIJON MUSTARD

1/4 TSP SALT

1/4 TSP PAPRIKA

2 TBSP DRIED SAGE

FRESH GROUND BLACK PEPPER

4, 4 OZ WHITEFISH FILLETS

Whisk the egg together with a teaspoon of olive oil, mustard, salt, paprika, sage, and pepper. Place in the refrigerator until chilled. Preheat oven to 400°F and rinse & pat dry the fish fillets. Place a skillet in the oven and let heat up then add 2 tsp of olive oil to the pan. Cover both sides of the fillets with the mustard and place into the skillet. Move the skillet back into the oven and cook for about 5 minutes, turn the fish then set your oven to broil and cook for another 5 minutes until golden brown on top. Serve hot.

DESSERT RECIPES

1. Creme Brule

Servings = 4 >> Serving size =1 custard

Cooking Time = 90 Minutes

2 CUPS 2% MILK

1/2 CUP NON-FAT DRY MILK POWDER

1 TSP PURE VANILLA EXTRACT

6 TBSP STEVIA OR SPLENDA

1/8 TSP SALT

2 LARGE EGG YOLKS

8 TSP SUGAR

Take out a small sauce pan and mix in the milk, milk powder, and vanilla. Heat until mix reaches 180°F. The mix will just start to boil & froth up. Remove from heat and let cool fully. After the milk mixture is cool preheat the oven to 300°F. Fill a roasting pan with water to about 3/4 of the way up a 1 cup ramekin dish. Place the roasting pan in the oven until the water is hot. With a stainless mixing bowl, mix in Splenda, egg yolk, and salt until smooth. Pour the milk mix into the egg mix and whisk until blended. Split the mix up into the ramekins and set each in the water-filled roasting pan. Cook for an hour and let cool for a half an hour while still in the water-filled pan. Cover with plastic wrap and place each ramekin in the fridge overnight. Put 2 tsps of sugar over the top of each ramekin and using a blowtorch, melt the sugar until golden brown. Serve chilled.

2. Cheesecake

Servings = 12 >> Serving size =1/12 pie

Cooking Time = 240 Minutes

16 SQUARES LOW-FAT GRAHAM CRACKERS

1 TBSP HONEY

1 LARGE EGG WHITE

8 OZ NON-FAT CREAM CHEESE

8 OZ REDUCED-FAT CREAM CHEESE

1 CUP NON-FAT SOUR CREAM

1 CUP 1% COTTAGE CHEESE

1 CUP GRANULATED STEVIA OR SPLENDA

1 TSP PURE VANILLA EXTRACT

1/4 CUP FRESH LEMON JUICE

1, 4 OZ CARTON EGG SUBSTITUTE

1/4 TSP SALT

3 EGG WHITES (FOR FILLING)

Preheat the oven to 300°F and get a springform pan. Remove the sides and place the bottom of the pan on two squares of aluminum foil. Fold the foil to the side can slip down over. The foil will end up on the inside of the pan on the sides and on the outside of the pan on the bottom. Fill a roasting pan larger than the springform with water and place in the oven to heat up. Chop graham crackers in a food processor until fine. Pour honey into the top of the processor until blended well. In a large mixing bowl, whisk one egg until frothy. Blend the egg whites and the cracker mix together and press into the springform. Bake in the oven for 15 minutes. Remove and let cool. In the food processor, mix together all other ingredients except the 3 egg whites. In another mixing bowl, whisk egg whites until stiff peaks. Fold the egg whites and mix together then pour into springform with crust fully baked. Place pan into hot water bath pan and bake for an hour. Turn off the oven, remove the water bath pan, and return the cheesecake to the oven. Let sit inside the oven for another 2 hours until cool. Chill before serving.

3. Yogurt Popsicles

Servings = 6 >> Serving size =1 six OZ pop

Cooking Time = 30 Minutes

1 1/2 CUPS FRESH OR FROZEN PEACHES

2/3 CUP NON-FAT YOGURT

1/3 CUP 1% COTTAGE CHEESE

1/4 CUP GRANULATED STEVIA OR SPLENDA

Put all ingredients into blender and blend until nice and smooth. Pour into popsicle molds and freeze for about 2-3 hours. To serve, you can run the outside of the mold under hot water to easily loosen the pops.

4. Pumpkin Tarts

Servings = 6 >> Serving size =1 tart

Cooking Time = 90 Minutes

18 GINGER SNAPS

1 TBSP UNSALTED BUTTER

3/4 CUP GRANULATED STEVIA OR SPLENDA

1/4 TSP SALT

1 TSP GROUND CINNAMON

1/4 TSP GROUND GINGER

1/4 TSP GROUND CLOVES

1 TSP PURE VANILLA EXTRACT

1 CUP PUMPKIN

1/2 CUP 2% MILK

4 OZ EGG SUBSTITUTE

Preheat the oven to 300°F then grind up the ginger snaps in a food processor. Divvy up the mix into 6 different tart pans, compact each one then stick in the oven to bake for about 15 minutes. Get a double boiler out and whisk together all ingredients over high heat until it begins to thicken up. Pour into the tart crusts and bake for 45 minutes. Chill before serving.

5. Key Lime

Servings = 4 >> Serving size =1 four OZ pop

Cooking Time = 30 Minutes

1/2 CUP NON-FAT YOGURT

1/4 CUP 1% COTTAGE CHEESE

1/4 CUP STEVIA OR SPLENDA

1/4 CUP LIME JUICE

Put all ingredients into a blender and puree until smooth. Pour into popsicle molds and place into the freezer for about 3-4 hours. You can run the mold under hot water to loosen the popsicles to serve.

6. Angel Food Cake

Servings = 6-8

Cooking Time = 60 Minutes

1 CUP SUPERFINE SUGAR, DIVIDED INTO 3/4 CUP AND 1/4 CUP PORTIONS

1 CUP SIFTED CAKE FLOUR

12 LARGE EGG WHITES, AT ROOM TEMPERATURE

1 TEASPOON CREAM OF TARTAR

1/2 TEASPOON SALT

2 TEASPOONS VANILLA EXTRACT

Preheat oven to 375°F then in a large bowl whisk three quarters of the sugar, and all the flour. In a separate bowl, beat egg whites until thick. Add cream of tartar, salt, and vanilla and beat until peaks form. Mix in the remaining sugar. Bring together both mixtures, then pour into a non-stick tube pan. Bake for about a half an hour, using a toothpick to test in the center to check for done-ness. Let cool then serve.

7. Berry Cobbler

Servings = 6-8

Cooking Time = 60 Minutes

2 CUPS ALL-PURPOSE FLOUR

1 CUP WHITE SUGAR

2 1/2 TEASPOONS BAKING POWDER

1/2 TEASPOON SALT

3 TABLESPOONS BUTTER, MELTED

2/3 CUP MILK

1-TEASPOON VANILLA

1 EGG, BEATEN

2 CUPS OF RASPBERRIES (BLACKBERRIES, CRANBERRIES OR BLUEBERRIES CAN BE SUBSTITUTED)

Preheat oven to 350°F then spray nonstick cooking oil into a square baking pan. Blend together flour, sugar, baking powder, and salt in a large mixing bowl. Bring in all other ingredients. Pour into pan and bake for 45 minutes until the top layer is tight and firm.

8. Apple Dumplings

Servings = 4

Cooking Time = 60 Minutes

4 LARGE GOLDEN APPLES WITH STEMS

1 TABLESPOON BUTTER

2 TABLESPOONS LIGHTLY TOASTED CHOPPED PECANS

2 TABLESPOONS BROWN SUGAR

1/2 TEASPOON GROUND CINNAMON

8 SHEETS FROZEN PHYLLO DOUGH, THAWED (KEEP COVERED TO PREVENT DRYING OUT)

2 TABLESPOONS MAPLE SYRUP

Preparation:

Preheat oven to 350°F and spray a cookie sheet with cooking oil. Peel apples and leave stems on each; cut the bottom of the apple flat so they will stand up straight with ease. Cut out the core of each apple using a melon-baller from the bottom of the apple. While holding the apple upside down, fill each cored out apple cavity with butter, pecans, brown sugar, and cinnamon. Take 2 phyllo dough sheets and spray with cooking oil, then press apple stem through the dough wrapping the dough around the bottom of the apple; place on baking sheet and repeat until all apples are done. Bake apples for about 45 minutes until dough is lightly browned. Drizzle maple syrup over each dumpling before serving; serve warm or chilled.

9. Pound Cake

Servings = 6-8

Cooking Time = 60 Minutes

2 CUPS FLOUR

1 TABLESPOON BAKING POWDER

1/4 TEASPOON SALT

1/2 CUP BUTTER, SOFTENED

1 1/2 CUPS SUGAR

4 EGG WHITES, LIGHTLY BEATEN

1 1/2 CUPS FAT-FREE SOUR CREAM

2 TEASPOONS VANILLA EXTRACT

Preheat oven to 350°F and spray a bundt pan with cooking oil. In a large mixing bowl, mix together the flour, baking powder, and salt. Set aside then in a separate bowl, mix together sugar and butter. Add egg whites, sour cream, and vanilla then mix well. Bring two mixtures together then pour into bundt pan. Bake for about an hour, using a toothpick to test done-ness. Cool before serving, and sprinkle a bit of powdered sugar over each piece.

10. Banana Cupcakes

Servings = 12

Cooking Time = 60 Minutes

1 CUP FLOUR

1/2 TEASPOON BAKING SODA

1/4 TEASPOON SALT

1/2 TEASPOON GROUND CINNAMON

3/4 GRANULATED SUGAR

1/4 CUP BUTTER

1 TEASPOON VANILLA EXTRACT

1/2 CUP MASHED RIPE BANANAS

4 LARGE EGG WHITES

1/4 CUP FAT-FREE SOUR CREAM

FROSTING - 1 1/2 CUPS POWDERED SUGAR

FROSTING - 8 OZ FAT-FREE CREAM CHEESE, SOFTENED

FROSTING - 1 TEASPOON VANILLA EXTRACT

Preheat oven to 350°F and spray a 12 muffin tin with cooking oil. In a mixing bowl, bring together flour, baking soda, salt, and cinnamon. In another bowl, mix sugar and butter. Add bananas and egg whites to the sugar mix and beat together well. Combine both mixtures then spoon into muffin tin. Bake for about a half an hour, testing with a toothpick to ensure doneness. Make the frosting by beating together the three frosting ingredients then spread over each cupcake.

CPSIA information can be obtained
at www.ICGtesting.com
Printed in the USA
LVHW021040210222
711618LV00009B/720